BIOCATALYTIC TECHNOLOGY AND NANOTECHNOLOGY

Biocatalytic Technology and Nanotechnology

G. E. Zaikov
Editor

Nova Science Publishers, Inc.
New York

Production Coordinator: Donna Dennis
Coordinating Editor: Tatiana Shohov
Senior Production Editors: Susan Boriotti and Donna Dennis
Production Editors: Marius Andronie and Rusudan Razmadze
Office Manager: Annette Hellinger
Graphic Design: Magdalena Nuñez,
Editorial Production: Maya Columbus, Aloysha Klestov, Vladimir Klestov,
Matthew Kozlowski and Lorna Loperfido
Circulation: Ave Maria Gonzalez, Vera Popovic, Luis Aviles, Jonathan Boriotti, Alexandra Columbus, Raymond Davis, Cathy DeGregory, Melissa Diaz, Marlene Nuñez, Jeannie Pappas and Frankie Punger
Communications and Acquisitions: Serge P. Shohov

Library of Congress Cataloging-in-Publication Data
Biocatalytic technology and nanotechnology / G. E. Zaikov et al., editor.
p. cm.
Includes bibliographical references and index.
ISBN 1-59454-117-5 (hardcover)
1. Nanotechnology. 2. Biotechnology.
[DNLM: 1. Mamotechnology--methods. 2. Biomedical Technology--methods. 3. Biotransformation. 4. Catalysis. QT 36 B61455 2004] I. I. Zaikov, Gennadiæi Efremovich.
TP248.25.N35B54 2004
736'.982--dc22 2004014092

400 Oser Ave, Suite 1600
Hauppauge, New York 11788-3619
Tele. 631-231-7269 Fax 631-231-8175
e-mail: Novascience@earthlink.net
Web Site: http://www.novapublishers.com

Printed in the United States of America

CONTENTS

ACKNOWLEDGEMENTS

We would like to thank Dr. Larisa P. Krylova who helped us very much during preparation of this volume.

G.E.Zaikov,
Prof., Member of Directorium,
N.M.Emanuel Institute of Biochemical Physics,
Russian Academy of Sciences.
4 Kosygin st., Moscow- 119991, Russia
Fax 7 095 137 41 01
E-mail chembio@sky,chph.ras.ru

In: Biocatalytic Technology and Nanotechnology ISBN 1-59454-117-5
Editor: G. E. Zaikov, pp. 1-27

Chapter 1

ORGANIZED PLANAR BIO-MOLECULAR AND HYBRID BIO-ORGANIC-INORGANIC NANOSTRUCTURES

G. B. Khomutov[*]
Faculty of Physics, M.V. Lomonosov Moscow State University

ABSTRACT

A number of new organized low-dimensional bio-molecular and hybrid bio-organic-inorganic nanostructures were obtained using new developed synthetic and assembling nanofabrication methods. The methods are based on the surface and interfacial interactions, biomimetic and bio-inspired strategies including biomineralization, self-assembling and self-organization principles. The examples of obtained nanostructures include new organized ultrathin nanostructured polymeric and nanocomposite films obtained with the use of monolayer polyelectrolyte complexes formed at the gas-aqueous phase interface, and Langmuir monolayer technology. The structural components of the films were amphiphilic polycation, DNA and surfactant molecules, organized arrays of inorganic semiconductor (CdS) and iron oxide (maggemite and magnetite) nanoparticles, nanorods, molecular ligand-stabilized metallic nanoclusters. Also, results on the fabrication and of multicompartment and porous polymeric films with nanostructured surfaces, and on formation of organized planar organic-inorganic nanostructures are presented. The methods developed can be perspective for investigation of fundamental mechanisms of nano-scale structural organization and transformations in various molecular (including bio-molecular) structures, and for development of new low-dimensional nanostructures, functional controlled-morphology nanomaterials, nanostructured films and coatings with advanced properties and potential for nanobiotechnological applications.

Keywords: DNA, Polycation, Complex, Liquid-gas interface, Monolayer, Nanoparticles, Nanoclusters, Low-dimensional nanostructures, Nanobiotechnology.

[*] Address for correspondence: Faculty of Physics, Moscow State University, Lenin Gory, 119992 Moscow, Russia. Fax: (007)-(095)-939-1195; Tel: (007)-(095)-939-3025; E-mail: GBK@phys.msu.ru

1. INTRODUCTION

Nanometer-scale controlled and organized technological processes, materials and devices are subjects of nanotechnology. Progress in nanotechnology is dependent on advances in nanoscience which is substantially interdisciplinary field based on nano-physics and nano-chemistry studying physical and chemical interactions at the nano-scale, fundamental mechanisms of nano-sclale structure formation and transformation processes, physical and chemical properties of surfaces and interfaces, low-dimensional systems, supramolecular structures and nanostructures, including biological structures.

Nanobiotechnology can be considered as a field of nanotechnology concerned with development of effective approaches to control the processes of nano-scale structural organization and functioning in biological, bio-organic and hybrid bio-organic-inorganic systems, what is of principal importance for advancements in a wide number of practical fields related to living systems, as medicine, bioengineering, advanced sensors, agriculture, etc. At the same time, a wide range of natural biological structures including proteins, lipid membranes and nucleic acids demonstrate remarkable properties for self-assembly, self-organization and self-replication. Various highly-organized inorganic (including magnetic) and hybrid organic-inorganic nanostructures are synthesized in biological and molecular structures via the biomineralization processes in which key role is played by the nature, composition and organization of molecular matrix interacting with inorganic phase [1, 2, 3]. The application of biomolecular assembly processes and principles to formation of synthetic or hybrid functional nanostructures and nanostructured materials can be useful for development of cost-effective nanofabrication methods in nanotechnology, especially taking into account that such synthetic procedures and building up of nanostructures being carried out at ambient and ecologically friendly conditions with high reproducibility of the structure and properties of the resulting nanomaterials characteristic for natural biological systems.

Polymer-based films and composites are characterized by high mechanical stability, rich structural and functional variety, processability and relatively low cost. Cost-effective synthesis and assembling of polymeric nanostructured materials and films with controlled composition and structural organization down to the nano-scale level of individual molecules is a challenge now with potential for new generation of advanced functional materials and coatings. Fabrication and study of organized hybrid nanostructures with integrated biological, polymeric and/or inorganic building blocks can be important for nano-biotechnological and other applications. It can result in development of new advanced materials with high functional specificity and effectiveness characteristic for biological systems along with enhanced processability and applicability due to the synthetic polymeric and inorganic components. In particularly, DNA molecules are promising candidates for nanobiotechnology building blocks to construct nano-scale wires, scaffolds and frameworks due to the unique DNA recognition capabilities, physicochemical and mechanical stability, and synthetic availability of practically any desired nucleotide sequences and lengths.

This contribution describes a number of new synthetic and assembling nanofabrication methods which can be related to nanobiotechnology and were introduced and developed in our group. The methods are based on the surface and interfacial interactions, biomimetic and bio-inspired strategies including biomineralization, self-assembling and self-organization principles. A number of new organized low-dimensional bio-molecular and hybrid bio-organic-inorganic nanostructures were obtained using the developed methods and were characterized by scanning probe microscopy, scanning electron microscopy (SEM) and transmission electron microscopy (TEM) techniques.

2. EXPERIMENTAL SECTION

Stearic acid (SA), arachidonic acid (AA), octadecyl amine (ODA), phosphatidyl choline dipalmitoyl (PDP), Salmon thymus native DNA (Na salt), Cytochrome ***c*** (horse heart), Poly(ethylenimine) (PEI) MW 70000, Sodium poly(styrene sulfonate)-Na salt (PSS) MW 70000, poly(allylamine hydrochloride) (PAH) MW 50.000, n-decane, oleic acid, $CdCl_2$, $FeCl_3$, NaCl were obtained from Sigma/Aldrich. All chemicals were purchased and used as supplied. Iron pentacarbonyl $Fe(CO)_5$ was obtained from Alfa Inorganic. Palladium acetate was obtained from Fluka. Metal-organic compounds $Au(P(C_6H_5)_3)Cl$ and $Pt_5(CO)_6[P(C_6H_5)_3]_4$ were synthesized by Prof. S.P. Gubin in accordance with known procedures [4]. Aqueous suspension of cationic CdSe nanorods (3×30 nm) was supplied by Dr. M. Artemyev. Water-insoluble amphiphilic polycation poly-4-vinilpyridine (PVP) with 16% and 20% of cationic cetylpyridinium groups (PVP-16 and PVP-20, correspondingly) was synthesized via the known procedures [5]. To obtain amphiphilic polycation, PVP fraction with degree of polymerization 1100 was prepared and then quaternized with cetyl bromide as described in [6]. Linear charge density as well as hydrophilic-hydrophobic balance of the quaternized PVP derivatives can be controlled easily via varying the extent of N-alkylation and the nature of alkyl groups. Milli-Q water purification system was used to produce water with an average resistivity of 18 MΩ-cm for all experiments. Raw emulsions were prepared from n-decane and water (1:10 ratio) by intensive mixing. Formation of Langmuir monolayers, surface pressure-monolayer area (π-A) isotherm measurements and monolayer transfer to the solid substrates with formation of Langmuir-Blodgett (LB) films were carried out on a fully automatic conventional Teflon trough at 21 °C as described elsewhere [7]. Surface pressure was measured with Wilhelmy plate balance. Mixed Langmuir monolayers at the aqueous phase-gas interface were formed by spreading a chloroform solution of surfactants and/or metal-organic compounds. The floating monolayers were compressed by a mobile Teflon barrier at a speed of ~3 $Å^2$/molecule×min and then deposited onto the solid substrates at a constant surface pressure (20 - 25 mN/m), temperature and substrate dipping speed, using the conventional horizontal or vertical substrate lifting methods with good transfer ratios. DNA/PVP-16 and DNA/PVP-20 complex LB films were formed by deposition of complex monolayer formed by amphiphilic polycation and DNA molecules bound with cationic monolayer from the aqueous phase.

Mica substrates were used for AFM investigations and were freshly cleaved immediately before monolayer deposition. Samples for TEM measurements were prepared by nanoparticulate monolayer deposition from aqueous subphase surface onto the Formwar film supported by the copper grid (diameter=3 mm). Highly oriented pyrolytic graphite (HOPG) was used as a deposition substrate for investigations of monolayer films by STM. The polished silicon plates (with a native oxide layer, 0.3-0.5 nm thick) were used as a substrate material for polymeric films deposition for SEM measurements.

To synthesize iron-containing magnetic nanoparticles interfacially in a monolayer we used the UV decomposition (UV irradiation from 300 mW conventional UV source, $\lambda \cong 300$ nm) of iron pentacarbonyl $Fe(CO)_5$ at the ambient temperature (21 °C) in a mixed Langmuir monolayer formed by spreading an appropriate amount of the chloroform solution of iron pentacarbonyl with SA on the surface of purified water (pH=5.6) as described in [8]. $Fe(CO)_5$ is a volatile water-insoluble metal-organic compound widely used in the chemical vapor deposition technique, with gas phase CO and iron and/or iron oxycarbide species as final products, at normal conditions it is a liquid with a tendency to evaporate slowly. Spreading solutions were prepared by dissolving SA and iron pentacarbonyl in chloroform to give concentration of 1×10^{-4} M SA molecules. Initial $Fe(CO)_5$/SA ratio in a monolayer was 10:1.

To synthesize palladium and gold nanoparticles, the mixed spreading solutions of water-insoluble palladium acetate $Pd_3(CH_3COO)_6$ or $Au(P(C_6H_5)_3)Cl$ with surfactants in chloroform were prepared (precursor/surfactant ratio was 3:1 and 1:3). Spreading solution was then deposited onto the surface of aqueous subphase containing sodium borohydride as a reducing agent ($NaBH_4$ concentration was 5×10^{-3} M). Nanoparticles were synthesized in a mixed precursor and surfactant Langmuir monolayer formed after solvent evaporation on the surface of borohydride solution. Nanoparticles and nanostructures were formed in a 2-D gas phase of a monolayer (at very low or no surface pressure) where in-plane diffusion of the monolayer components and their self-organization was possible. The metallic nature of nanoparticles was established using TEM technique. The compression of a monolayer with growing nanoparticles to the monolayer condensed state and following deposition of monolayer onto the solid substrate stopped the diffusion-mediated processes in the monolayer and fixed effectively the grown nanostructures.

Iron oxide nanoparticles were generated via DNA templating. Nanoparticles were formed by incubation of corresponding precursor film containing Fe^{3+} cations (DNA/Fe^{3+}/PVP-16 complex film) in the sodium borohydride (5×10^{-4} M) or ascorbic acid (1×10^{-3} M) solutions followed by the film incubation in the high pH aqueous media (pH=10) at ambient conditions for 1 or 2 hours. The preliminary analyses of the generated iron-containing nanoparticles using electron diffraction technique pointed to the iron oxide nature (magnetite and maggemite phases) of obtained nanoparticles. DNA/Fe^{3+}/PVP-16 complex film was formed via the incubation of DNA/PVP-16 complex LB film in the $FeCl_3$ solution (2×10^{-4} M $FeCl_3$, pH=2.5).

Semiconductor CdS nanoparticles were synthesized via the incubation of corresponding precursor film containing Cd^{2+} cations (DNA/Cd^{2+}/PVP-16 complex film) in the H_2S atmosphere for 2 hours. DNA/Cd^{2+}/PVP-16 complex film was formed via the incubation of DNA/PVP-16 LB film in the $CdCl_2$ solution (2×10^{-4} M $CdCl_2$, pH=6.0) for 1 hour.

STM microtopographic images were obtained by recording the tip height at a constant tunnel current (0.2 nA) in a modified Nanoscop STM device (Digital Instruments) at an ambient temperature (21 ^{o}C). The images were stable and reproducible.

AFM measurements were performed with the use of Solver P47-SPM-MDT scanning probe microscope (NT MDT Ltd., Moscow, Russia) and Nanoscop III (Digital Instruments) in a tapping mode. Images were measured in air at ambient temperature (21 ^{o}C) and were stable and reproducible.

TEM images of nanoparticles synthesized in Langmuir monolayer were obtained with the use of Jeol JEM-100B microscope.

Hitachi S-405A scanning electron microscope was used to image the surface of prepared films which were sputter-coated with 20 nm Pd/Pt layer on a IB-3 Eiko coater (Japan).

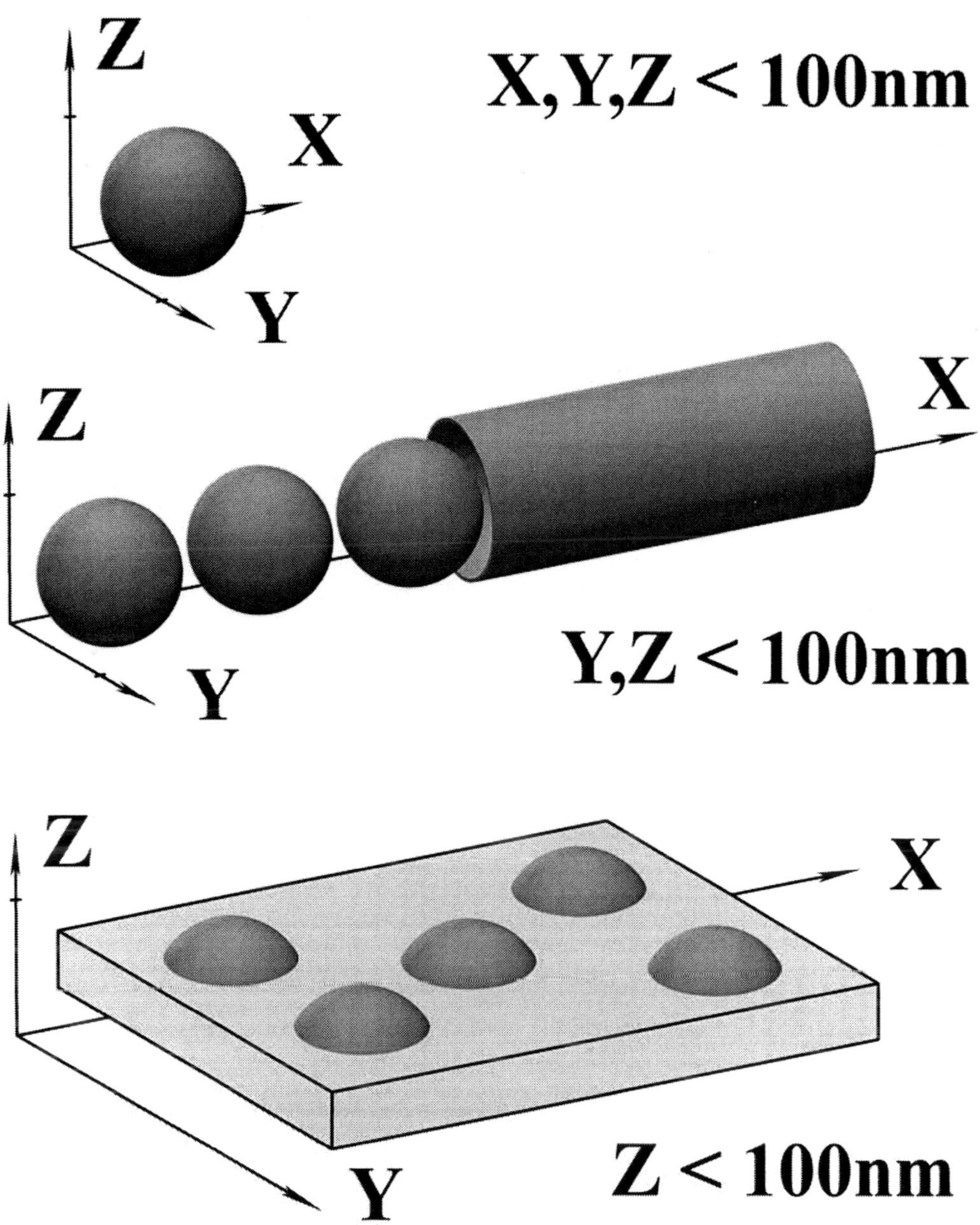

Figure 1. Schematical representation of zero-dimensional (0-D), one-dimensional (1-D) and two-dimensional (2-D) nanostructures.

3. Results and Discussion

Nanomaterials and low-dimensional nanostructures are expected to exhibit novel and significantly improved physical, chemical and other properties, as well as to offer opportunities for manifestation of new physical phenomena and processes as, for example, various quantum effects in optical and electronic properties of nanostructures [9-13]. Clusters, nanoparticles, nanorods and nanowires, long molecules as nanotubes and polynucleotides are currently considered as potential functional and structural building blocks for new advanced nanostructured materials, films, devices and circuits for nanoelectronics and nanotechnological (including nanobiotechnology) applications. The development and introduction of new low-cost methods for effective control of their structure, composition and purposeful nano-scale assembly and organization are now necessary. Fabrication of organized low-dimensional structures composed of nano-scale functional components is a principal step on the way to practical manufacturing of nanodevices. Various nanostructures which are perspective for nanotechnological applications can be classified in accordance with their dimensionality. Figure 1 presents schematically zero-dimensional (0-D), one-dimensional (1-D) and two-dimensional (2-D) nanostructures in which at least one linear structural parameter is less than 100 nm. 3-D nanostructures can be determined as non-planar structures and materials containing low-dimensional nanostructures as functional elements and building blocks. 0-D nanostructures (dots) are clusters, nanocrystals, nanoparticles, functional molecules, fullerenes, dispersions, nanocolloids, etc. 1-D nanostructures are chains, channels, nanowires, nanotubes, long molecules, nanofibres. 2-D nanostructures are layers, films, coatings, planar nanostructures and nanocomposites. Various nanoporous, nanocomposite and nanostructured organic and inorganic materials belong to 3-D nanostructures. Concerning nanobiotechnology, organized structures of various dimensionality from biomolecules (proteins, nucleic acids, supramolecular complexes, membranes), in vivo usable drugs and cell tagging agents, drug or gene delivery vectors, nanocapsules, nanoengineered tissue scaffold, nanostructured biomaterials and coatings for implants and prostheses, biochips – in vitro usable DNA chips, protein and drug screening arrays, DNA patterned structures and hybrid bio-organic-inorganic nanostructures are of current interest.

A number of examples of organized low-dimensional biomimetic, bio-molecular and hybrid bio-organic-inorganic nanostructures developed and studied in our group are presented below.

3.1. Nanocluster and Metalloprotein Containing 2-D Nanostructures

Langmuir-Blodgett technique has been proven to be an efficient tool for fabrication of organized two-dimensional arrays of nanoclusters, proteins, nanoparticles and nanowires [14-20]. We have introduced earlier a bio-inspired approach to fabrication of reproducible stable 2-D nanocluster nanostructures based on the formation of biomimetic mixed LB films consisting of inert amphiphile molecular matrix and guest chemically synthesized nanocluster molecules (Figure 2). Such nanostructures can serve as a model systems for investigations of basic mechanisms of membrane electron tunneling redox reactions and are perspective for development of room-temperature controlled single-electron tunneling molecular elements and devices [21]. The double tunnel junction (DTJ) structure "graphite substrate-nanocluster molecule-scanning tunneling microscope (STM) tip" was studied [22, 23] and effects related to single electron tunneling and discrete electronic levels spectrum were observed in such structures at room temperature using STM. Ligand-stabilized nanocluster molecules could prove to be promising components for nanoelectronic circuits: such compounds can be chemically synthesized in macroscopic quantities with uniform size, structure and composition, and, as a result, with absolutely reproducible properties of individual clusters what is of principal importance for creation of quantum nanoelectronic devices. Stabilizing organic ligand shell of the cluster prevents coalescence of clusters and allows to regulate with Angstrom accuracy the inter-cluster distances in the ordered arrays of clusters. Functional groups in the nanocluster ligand shell can allow the purposeful immobilization and organization of clusters on substrate surfaces or in 1-D, 2-D and 3-D systems. Using such approach a single-electron tunneling transistor (SET) based on a single nanocluster molecule was demonstrated at room temperature for the first time [24].Different molecular SET transistors with various nanocluster molecules having metal cores from 3 to 23 metal atoms used as a central transistor electrode were formed and studied successfully [10].

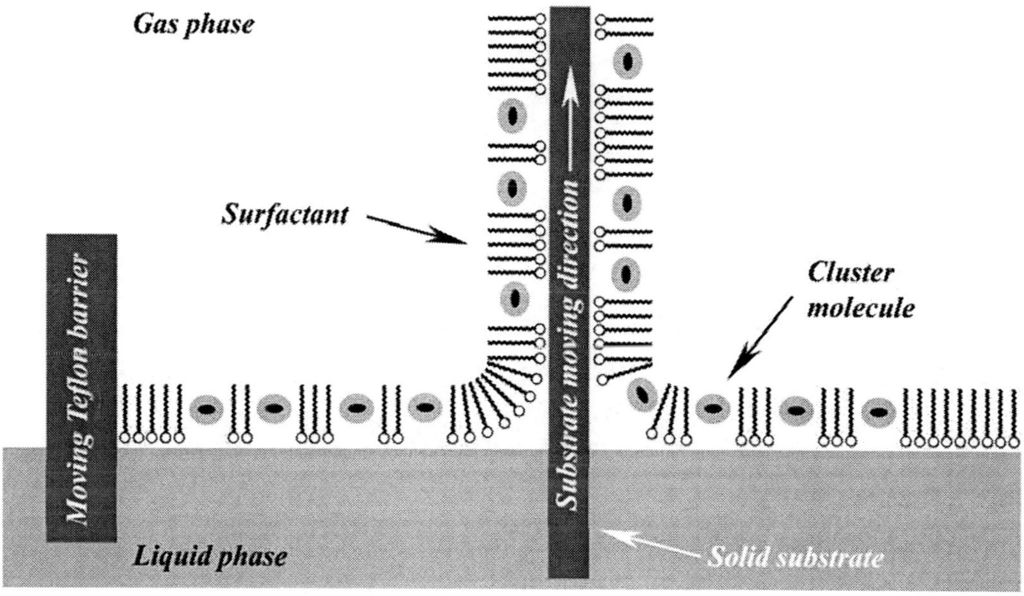

Figure 2. Scheme of fabrication of nanocluster containing 2-D molecular nanostructures via Langmuir-Blodgett monolayer technique.

In a sense, electron transporting redox metalloproteins are analogous in a number of features (core metal cluster with organic ligand shell, atomically reproducible structure) with metal-organic nanocluster molecules used in our studies. Similar complex electron tunneling effects were observed in STM spectroscopic studies of isolated fullerene molecules [25] and cytochrome ***c*** molecules [17] giving evidence for the similar sequential discrete electron tunneling mechanisms in such immobilized metalloprotein and nanocluster structures which can be of interest for development of bioelectronic and hybrid functional nanoelectronic devices with biological redox components integrated into synthetic nanostructures or vice versa. Figure 3 shows STM topographic images of nanocluster and cytochrome ***c*** monolayer LB films on graphite substrate. One can see the compact ordered two-dimensional array of $Pt_5(CO)_6[P(C_6H_5)_3]_4$ nanoclusters in the monolayer (Fig. 3a) with lattice parameters: $a = 28.0 \pm 4.0$ Å, $b = 20.0 \pm 4.0$ Å, $\alpha = 70^o$. Characteristic STM images of individual cytochrome c molecules with diameter ~ 3nm are seen on Fig. 3b. The presented data illustrate the possibilities for fabrication of highly-ordered 2-D structures from nanoclusters via simple interfacial monolayer technique.

a

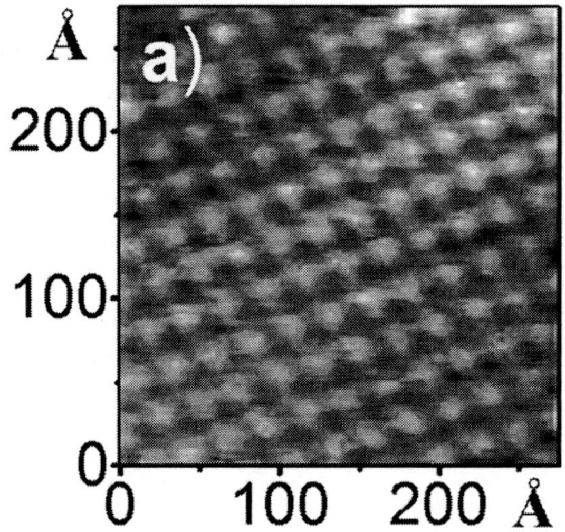

b

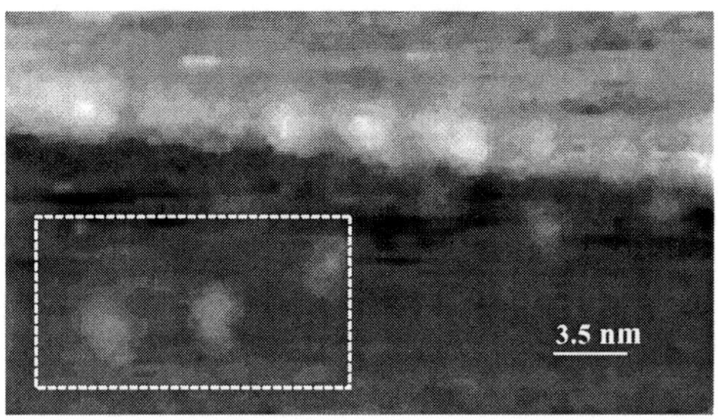

Figure 3. STM top view topographic images of $Pt_5(CO)_7[P(C_6H_5)_3]_4$ nanocluster and cytochrome ***c*** complex monolayers deposited by Shaefer's method onto the surface of highly oriented pyrolytic graphite substrate. Image **a)**: nanocluster monolayer (black-to-white vertical color scale is 0-1.5 nm); **b)**: cytochrome c monolayer (black-to-white vertical color scale is 0-**1.2** nm). Individual cytochrome c molecules are clearly visible in the area marked by the white frame.Temperature 21 °C.

3.2. Nano-Scale Organized Polymeric Films and Multicompartment, Porous and Capsulate Polymer Complex Film Materials and Coatings

It was found that the structure of deposited monolayers of amphiphilic polycation PVP-16 and PVP-20 was characterized by the ordered planar morphology giving evidence for quasi-parallel organization of polycation molecules in plane of the film. Figure 4 shows the characteristic AFM tapping mode topographic image (Images a) and b)) of 2-layer LB film of PVP-16 deposited onto the mica substrate after 10 min incubation of the PVP-16 Langmuir monolayer at low surface pressure value ($\pi \cong 0$) on the water subphase surface (pH=6). One can see that the film was macroscopically ordered with tightly packed characteristic structural elements (~ 33 nm in vertical direction, ~ 45 nm in horizontal direction, ~ 2 nm in height as follows from the fast Fourier transform spectrum analysis of the image a) and cross-section profile on Fig. 4c) and 4d), correspondingly). Similar nanostructured films were obtained with PVP-20. Such amphiphilic polyelectrolyte monolayer structure can be a result of the ordered surface micelle arrays formation which are known for LB films of diblock copolymers [26]. The tendency for linear quasi-parallel chain organization of surface micelles in PVP-16 LB films can be a result of smectic liquid crystal ordering of linear PVP-16 molecules on the aqueous subphase surface due to the effective electrostatic repulsive interaction between the positively charged links in a molecule and between extended polycation molecules in the monolayer. Also, effects of parallel organization of one-dimensional structures (wires) in Langmuir monolayer under compression can be involved [20]. Figure 5 demonstrates the possibilities for variation of polymeric film morphology via variation in the amphiphilic polycation Langmuir monolayer incubation time (Fig. 5a, nanoporous film) and composition of the monolayer (Fig. 5b, domain morphology in mixed amphiphilic polycation/ODA LB film).

Figures 6 and 7 demonstrate the morphologies of porous and composite capsulate polymeric multilayer films with layer-by-layer controlled composition, structure and properties. The method to form such structures includes the adsorption of template colloid latex particles or surfactant-stabilized emulsion droplets at the liquid/solid or liquid/gas interface with subsequent assembling of coating film via conventional layer-by-layer stepwise alternate adsorption procedure. Then immobilized template colloidal core can be decomposed with formation of holes and capsules in the film material via known procedures. Emulsion droplets can be easily loaded with various hydrophobic (oil in water emulsion) or hydrophilic (double-emulsion technique) compounds. Micro-porous bulk polymeric and inorganic materials can be also obtained with the use of emulsions via solidification of the bulk phase. Multilayer polyelectrolyte films composed of PSS and PAA were assembled on the silicon substrate with natural oxide layer, and the adsorption of different charged latcx particles, emulsion droplets and polyelectrolyte/emulsion complexes with subsequent encapsulation via the conventional layer-by-layer sequential polyelectrolyte multilayer deposition technique has been studied. Scanning electron microscopy has been used to monitor the morphology of the formed structures. Figure 6 represents the scanning electron micrographs of the deposited capsulate structure formed by the (oleic acid + decane) O/W emulsion complex with PAH on the surface of substrate coated by the PEI layer. In this case one can see characteristic micrometer-sized 3-D structures corresponding to the immobilized and fixed emulsion/polyelectrolyte complex droplets. SEM micrographs of different capsulated polyelectrolyte complex films are presented on the Figure 7. The regular submicrometer-size structural organizations of the films dependent on the reaction conditions are clear seen from the Figure 7. Figure 8 shows AFM tapping mode top view topographic images of the fine surface structure of deposited films formed by the (oleic acid + decane) O/W emulsion complex with PSS and PAH formed on the surface of substrate coated by the PEI layer and treated by chloroform. One can see ordered ultra-structural organization of the film with structural elements of about 400 nm in length due to the formation of presumably lamellar

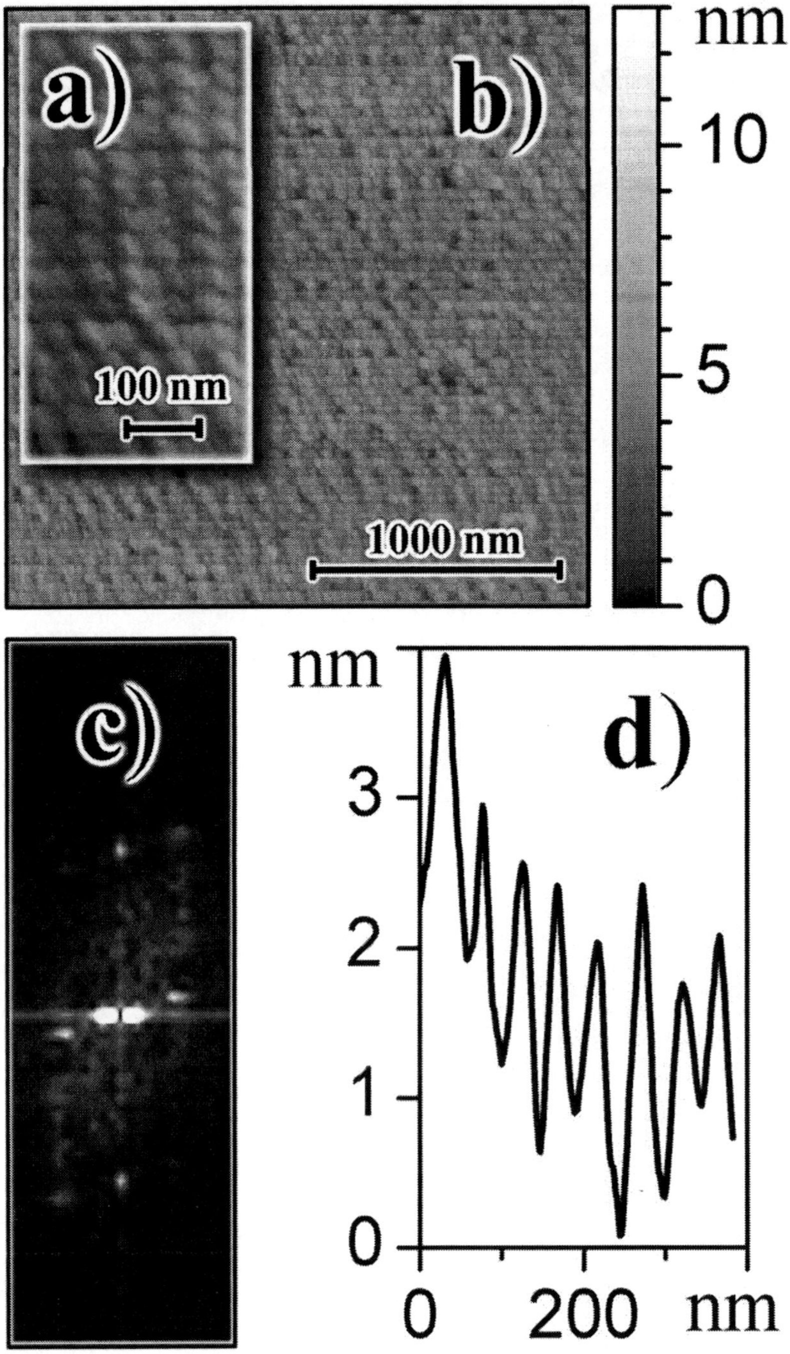

Figure 4. AFM tapping mode images of 2-layer LB film of PVP-16 deposited onto the mica substrate after 10 min incubation of the PVP-16 Langmuir monolayer at low surface pressure value ($\pi \cong 0$) on the water subphase (pH=6); Images **a**) and **b**): top view topographic images (black-to-white color height scale is 0-13 nm). Image **c**) Fourier transform spectrum of the image **a**). Curve **d**): characteristic cross-section profile of the image **a**) parallel to the X-axis.

a

b

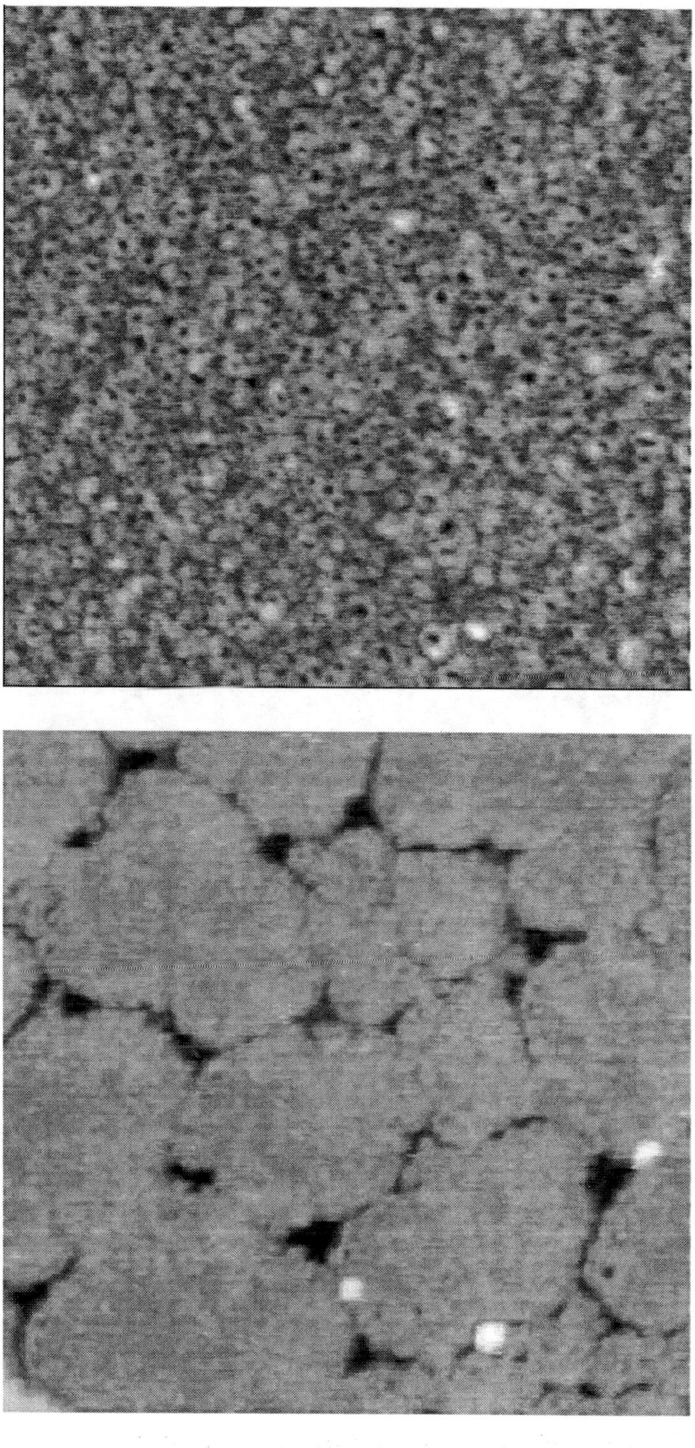

Figure 5. AFM tapping mode top view topographic images of polymeric 2-layer LB films on mica substrate. Image **a**): PVP-16 monolayer was deposited after 5 min incubation. Image **b**): mixed PVP-16 and ODA monolayer (stoichiometric ratio 1:1 for PVP monomer and ODA) deposited after 10 min incubation on the water surface.

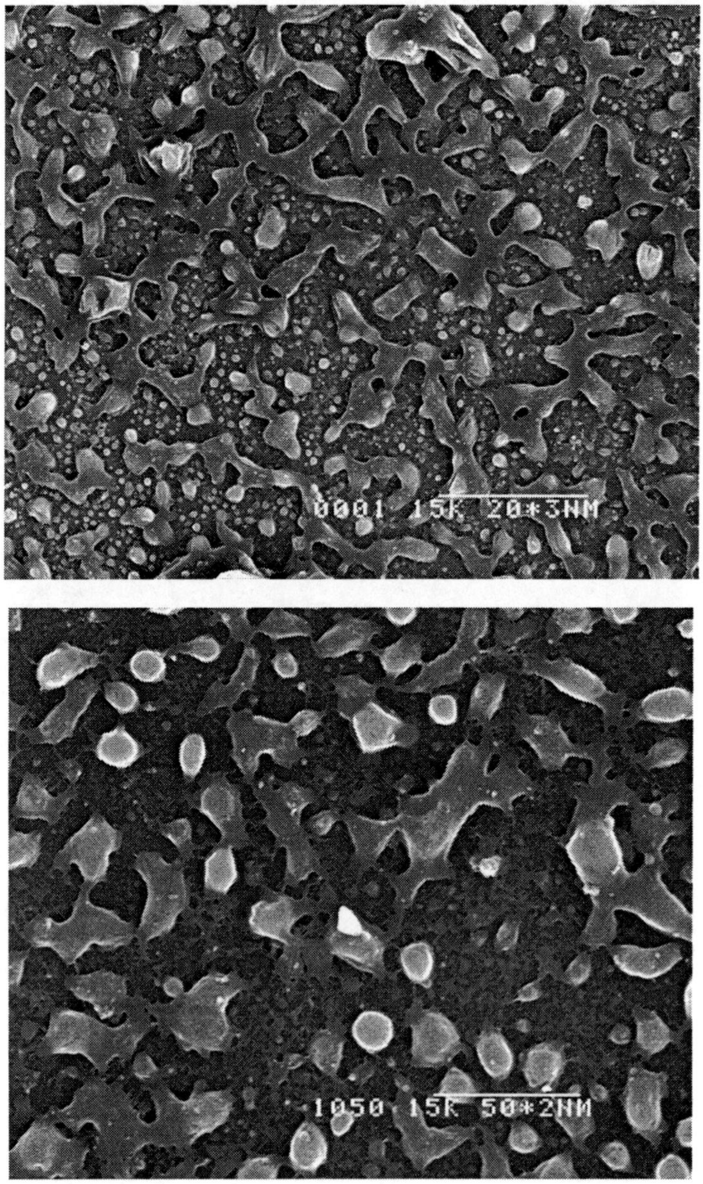

a

b

Figure 6. Scanning electron micrographs of the deposited film formed by (oleic acid+decane) O/W emulsion complex with PAH on the surface of substrate coated by the PEI layer, scale bar is 20 μm (image **a**) and 5 μm (image **b**).

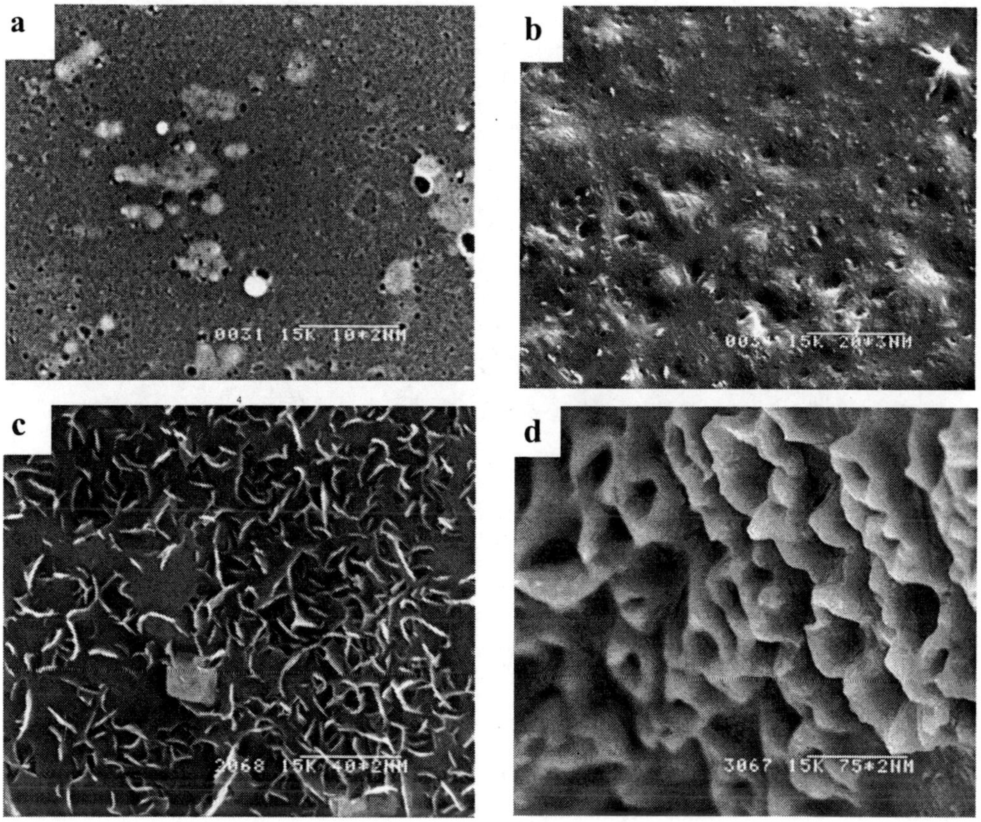

Figure 7. Scanning electron micrographs of capsulated and porous polyelectrolyte complex films. Image **a**): the film was formed by the deposition of (ODA+decane) O/W emulsion droplets on the surface of substrate coated by $(PAH/PSS)_3$ film with PSS outer layer in presence of PAH (monomer concentration 10^{-3} M), immersion time 10 min, and further deposition of 5 (PSS/PAH) layers, scale bar is 1 μm; Image **b**): condition of the film formation were the same but PAH concentration was 10^{-4} M, scale bar is 20 μm; Images **c**): (ODA+decane) O/W emulsion complex with PSS formed on the surface of substrate coated by $(PAH/PSS)_5$ film with PSS outer layer, scale bar is 4 μm; Image **d**): (ODA+decane) O/W emulsion complex with PAA formed on the surface of substrate coated by $(PAH/PSS)_5$ film with PSS outer layer, scale bar is 7.5 μm.

polyelectrolyte/surfactant complexes. Well known lamellar lipid/protein complexes are present in the blood and play substantial role in physiological processes. The results presented demonstrate the possibilities to create novel composite capsulated and porous polymeric films and coatings with sub-micrometer controlled structure. Such films could prove to be perspective for biotechnological and other applications due to the effective layer-by-layer control of its composition, structure and properties as mechanical stability and integrity, permeability, biocompatibility and surface functionality.

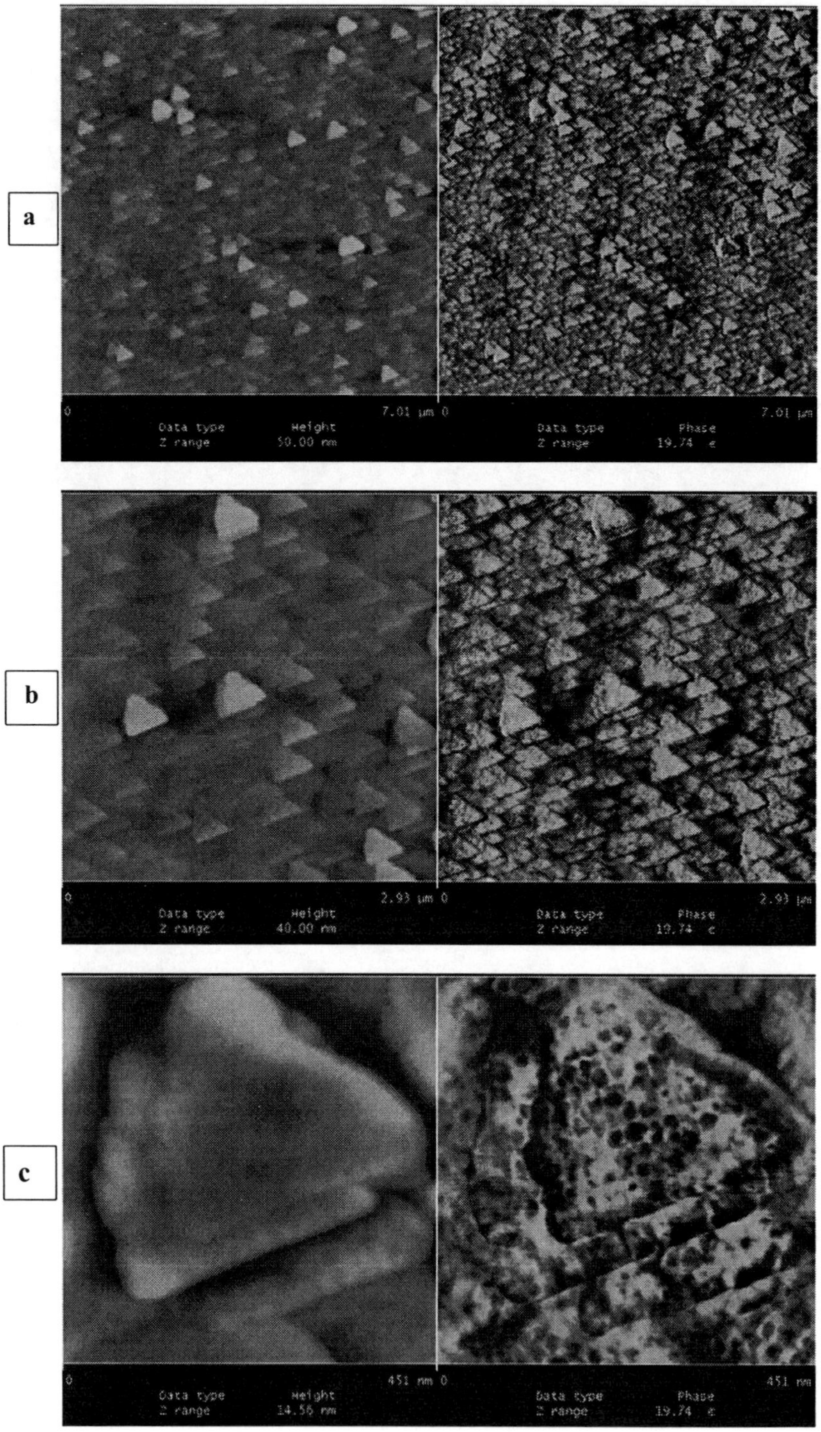

Figure 8. AFM tapping mode top view topographic images (left) and corresponding phase contrast images (right) of the fine surface structure of deposited films formed by the (oleic acid + decane) O/W emulsion complex with PSS and PAH on the surface of silicon substrate with natural oxide layer coated by the PEI layer and treated by chloroform. Image **a**): image size 7.01×7.01 μm^2, black-to-white vertical color scale is 0-50 nm; Image **b**): image size 2.93×2.93 μm^2, black-to-white vertical color scale is 0-40 nm; Image **c**): image size 451×451 nm^2, black-to-white vertical color scale is 0-14.5 nm.

3.3. Effects of Surfactants and Bio-Molecules on Interfacially Grown Inorganic Nanostructures

A novel method for synthesis of nanoparticles and formation of organized planar nanostructures based on the interfacial Langmuir monolayer technique has been introduced recently [8]. In that method nanoparticles are fabricated via the decomposition of an insoluble metal-organic precursor compounds in a monolayer at the gas/liquid interface. The ultimately thin and anisotropic dynamic monomolecular reaction system was realized by that method with the two-dimensional growth and organization of nanoparticles and nanostructures in the plain of a monolayer on the liquid surface. The possibilities for precursor and surfactant molecules to form true monolayer and the structure and homogeneity of the monolayer are substantial for this method and are dependent on the surfactant and precursor nature and monolayer compression extent. Thus, amphiphilic properties of precursor and its behavior in the mixed monolayer can be important for the 2-D synthesis method. In the 2-D synthesis method the properties of surfactants to form Langmuir monolayer and to passivate and stabilize growing clusters and nanoparticles are combined successfully.The important feature and advantage of the method is that the anisotropic 2-D synthesis of nanoparticles in this method takes place on the liquid substrate surface without interaction of growing nanoparticles with a solid surface. It opens new possibilities for elucidation the fine mechanisms of nucleation, growth and self-organization of nanophase materials at the nanometer-scale level. The other advantage of the method is the possibility to carry out synthesis of nanoparticles at the different physical states of the reaction media (under different compression extent of the monolayer): 2-D gas or 2-D liquid. Besides, the compression of the monolayer to the condensed state allows to stop the diffusion-controlled reactions in the monolayer and to fix effectively the growing nanoparticles at different growth process stages for subsequent characterization.

One embodiment of the method of interfacial 2-D synthesis of metallic nanoparticles can be the formation of a mixed monolayer composed of metal-organic precursor and surfactant molecules at the gas/liquid interface with subsequent chemical reduction of the metal to zero-valent state. In that case the ultimate version of a two-phase reducing system in which precursor phase represents an ultimately thin monomolecular structure is realized. Gold nanoparticles and nanostructures synthesized via the 2-D synthesis method are shown on Fig. 9. The analysis of selected area electron diffraction patterns obtained for the studied samples indicated to the polycrystalline metallic Au. Fig. 9a) represents the sample with Au nanoparticles synthesized in a mixed lipid Langmuir monolayer (initial $Au(P(C_6H_5)_3)Cl$/PDP ratio was 1:1) at the gas/sodium borohydride aqueous solution interface. The grown nanoparticles were organized in a quasi-linear aggregates in plane of the monolayer. Fig 9b) shows Au nanoparticles synthesized in a mixed uncompressed $Au(P(C_6H_5)_3)Cl$/ODA Langmuir monolayer. Image 9c) demonstrates the effect of 2-D self-organization of Au nanoparticles with formation of complex anisotropic planar nanostructures after monolayer incubation. Figure 9d) shows size distribution histogram of Au nanoparticles corresponding to the image 9b). It follows from the image 9b) that Au nanoparticles synthesized in a mixed ODA monolayer are characterized by rather small size (main diamcter ~ 1.5 nm) and narrow size distribution. Small size of synthesized gold nanoparticles allowed to observe SET effects at room temperature in the double barrier tunnel junction configuration "STM tip- Au nanoparticle-conducting HOPG substrate" [19].

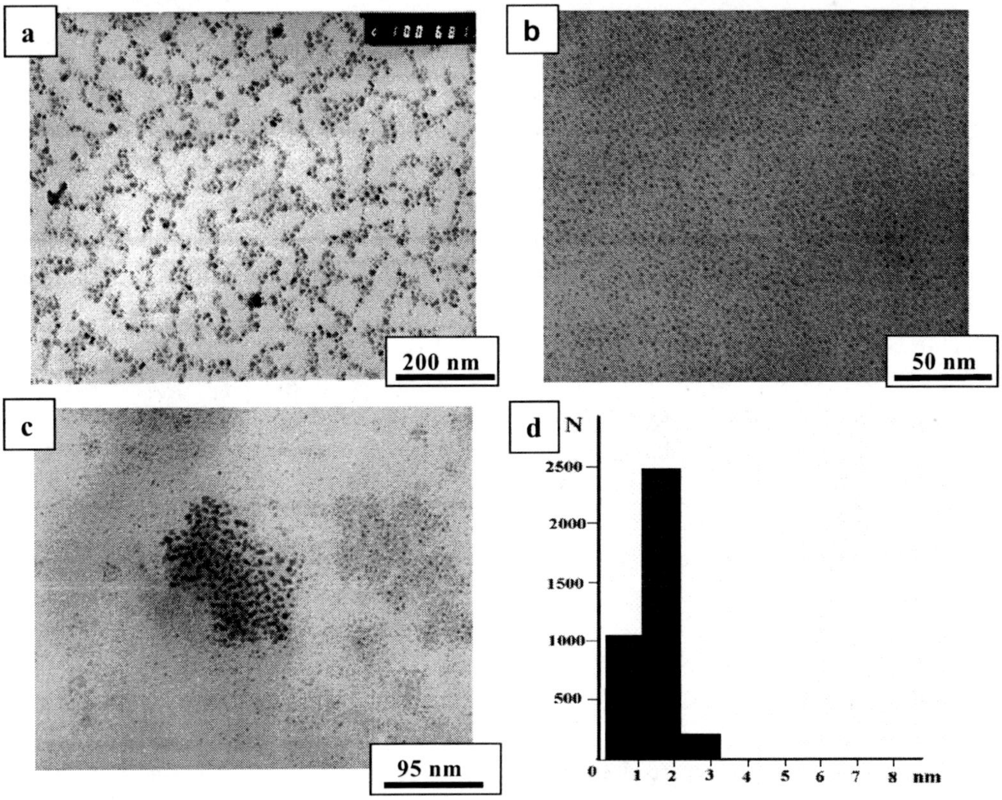

Figure 9. Transmission electron micrographs showing Au nanoparticles grown in Langmuir monolayer on the surface of sodium borohydride aqueous solution and deposited onto the copper grid with Formvar coating. Image **a**): sample with Au nanoparticles synthesized in a mixed Langmuir monolayer (initial $Au(P(C_6H_5)_3)Cl$/PDP ratio 1:1) at $\pi = 0$, incubation time 20 min, and deposited at $\pi = 18$ mN/m. Image **b**): Au nanoparticles synthesized in a mixed Langmuir monolayer (initial $Au(P(C_6H_5)_3)Cl$/ODA ratio 1:5) at $\pi = 0$, incubation time 20 min. Image **c**): $Au(P(C_6H_5)_3)Cl$/AA spreading solution with ratio 1:5 was used to form monolayer, incubation time 40 min. Image **d**): size distribution histogram of Au nanoparticles corresponding to the image b).

Figure 10 shows characteristic TEM images of Pd nanoparticles and organized planar Pd nanostructures synthesized in a mixed Langmuir monolayer formed by precursor $Pd_3(CH_3COO)_6$ and various surfactant molecules including lipids. One can see the dramatic effects of the monolayer composition and inorganic phase growth conditions on the morphology of resulting Pd nanostructures. Nanostructures with various morphologies were obtained: planar net-like and very high surface area structures(Fig. 10a and 10b), nano-organized planar labyrinth-like structures (Fig. 10c) and quasi-linear structures (Fig. 10e and 10f). Very small individual Pd nanoparticles (main size ~ 5 nm) were obtained in presence of DNA in the aqueous phase (Fig. 10d).

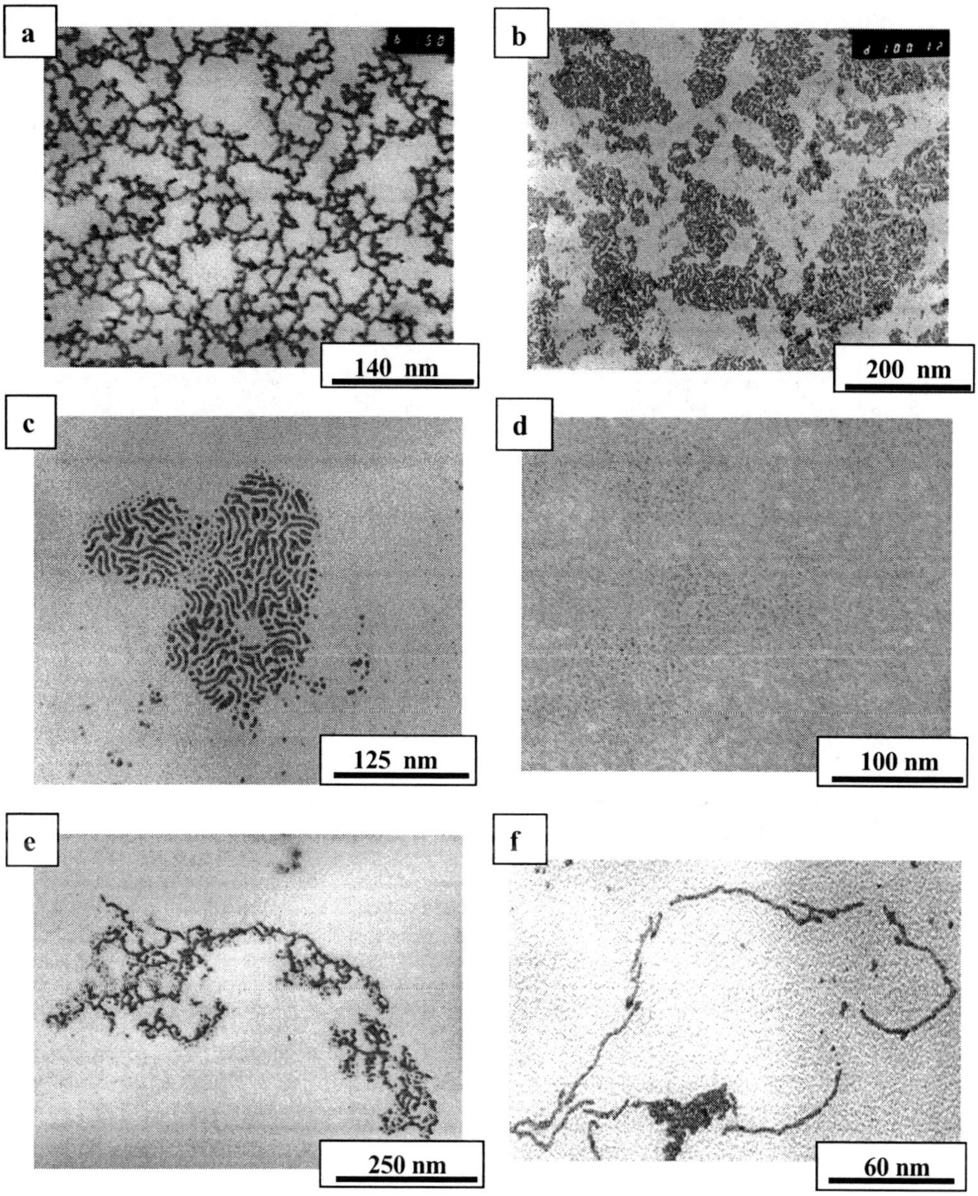

Figure 10. Transmission electron micrographs showing Pd nanoparticles synthesized in Langmuir monolayer at the gas/sodium borohydride solution interface at $\pi = 0$ and deposited onto the mica substrate at $\pi = 25$ mN/m. Image **a**): nano-net Pd structure; Image **b**): Pd nanostructures with very high surface/volume ratio formed in a monolayer with initial $Pd_3(CH_3COO)_6$/ODA ratio 3:1; Image **c**): nano-organized Pd nanostructure formed in a monolayer with initial $Pd_3(CH_3COO)_6$/ODA ratio 1:3; Image **d**): Pd nanoparticles formed in the presence of DNA (10^{-4} M per monomer) in aqueous subphase; Image **e**): extended Pd nanostructures formed in a monolayer with initial $Pd_3(CH_3COO)_6$/PDP ratio 1:1; Image **f**) Pd nanowires formed in a monolayer with initial $Pd_3(CH_3COO)_6$/AA ratio 1:1.

3.4. 1-D Nanostructures

Fabrication of 1-D nanostructures is generally more difficult task than formation of 2-D structures. Organized 1-D nanostructures are of great importance in development of various functional nanomaterials and nanodevices. Thus, concerning nanobiotechnology, sensors with very high sensitivity can be fabricated with the use of conducting 1-D nanostructures. The principal idea of such sensors is illustrated by Figure 11. In such device N sensitive (ligand binding) sites are arranged consecutively as linear structures on 1-D conductor between electrodes. Also, chains of closely-located receptors can be quasi-linear conducting functional structures in such device. If conductivity in such linear receptor system is sensitive enough to a single act of reception (for example, binding of one ligand to one of N binding sites), thus sensitivity of such sensor would be N times higher than in a sensor which can register only single act of ligand/receptor interaction. Various configurations of sensors with 1-D conductor sensitive to one ligand or to a number of ligands can be constructed via formation of homogeneous or heterogeneous 1-D receptor arrays (Fig. 11). Various strategies to form sensitive 1-D structures can be developed, in particularly, with the use of semiconducting nanowires or nanotubes.

Figure 12a shows 1-D chain structures of nanoclusters $Pt_5(CO)_6[P(C_6H_5)_3]_4$ formed in a mixed nanocluster/surfactant monolayer with appropriate nanocluster/surfactant ratio. Figure 12b demonstrates chains of magnetic iron-containing nanoparticles formed in a mixed surfactant Langmuir monolayer. Here inter-particle dipole-dipole interactions can be involved in formation of 1-D chain structures. Figure 13 illustrates schematically the idea of new approach to create nanoscale-ordered composite planar polymeric nanostructures with incorporated or grown structural or functional nanoscopic components. First, organized polymeric monolayer structure of amphiphilic polycation molecules is formed on the surface of a liquid phase and serves as an organizing stable monomolecular media. The possibility to form such structures was demonstrated by Fig. 4. Then, polymeric nanoscale-ordered nanocomposite film can be formed via the incorporation of previously prepared inorganic or organic functional components in the polymeric monolayer or via the interfacial synthesis of nanoparticles directly in the monolayer. Also, various low-dimensional nanostructures can be bound to the monolayer from the liquid subphase. Further deposition of such monolayer onto the solid substrates allows fabrication of organized ultrathin mono- and multilayer composite polymeric films and coatings. Such polymeric films with thickness down to a monolayer can be of use for nanotechnological applications because different functional nano-size elements (as guest molecules; ligand-stabilized nanoclusters and nanocrystals, metallic, oxidic or semiconducting nanoparticles, nanorods and nanowires, etc.) can be incorporated in such films to form ultimately thin highly-ordered stable planar composite polymeric nanostructures. It is possible to adsorb oppositely charged polyelectrolytes (or other compounds or colloids) from the subphase to the formed interfacial amphiphilic polyelectrolyte (or composite) monolayer what can improve stability of the film and broaden its functionality. The approach was realized for $Pt_5(CO)_6[P(C_6H_5)_3]_4$ nanocluster and PVP-16 monolayer [27].

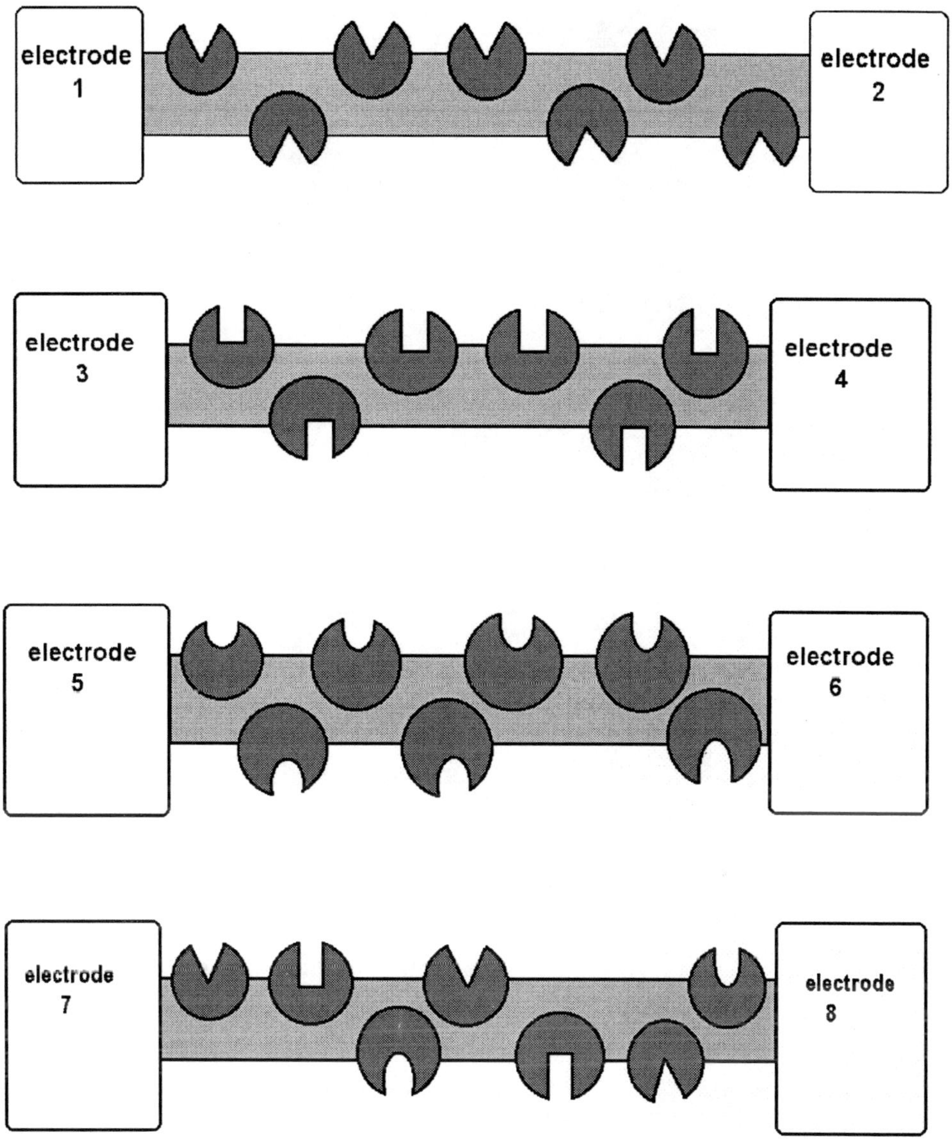

Figure 11. Scheme of 1-D sensor nanostructures. Chains of ligand-binding sites are formed between electrodes.

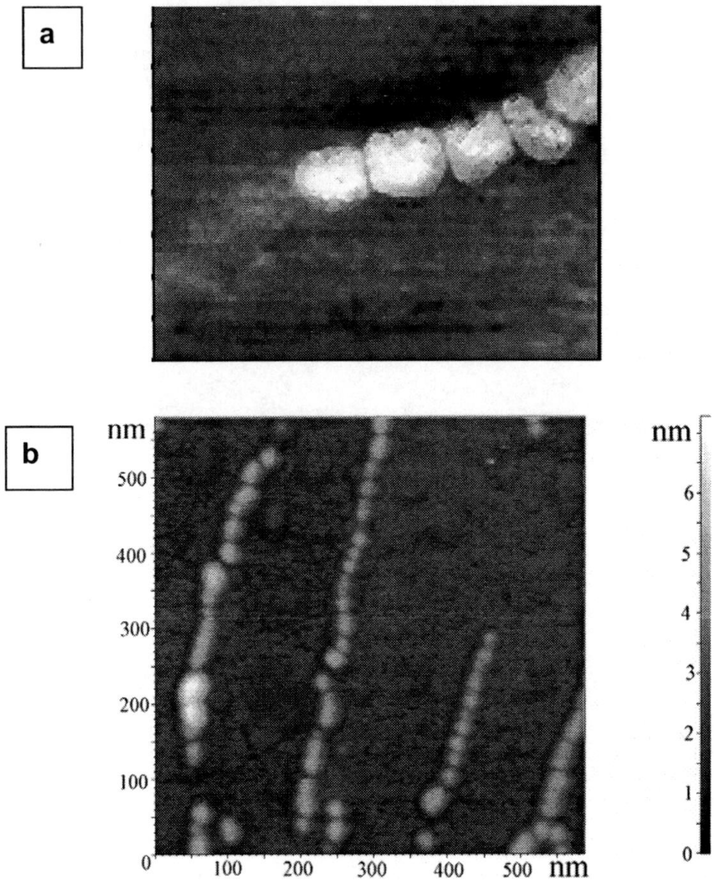

Figure 12. Image **a**): STM top view topographic image of chain of $Pt_5(CO)_6[P(C_6H_5)_3]_4$ nanocluster molecules formed in a mixed monolayer composed by cluster and stearic acid molecules with stoichiometric ratio 1:20, image size: 75×110 Å^2. Black-to-white vertical color scale is 0-1 nm. Image **b**): AFM tapping mode topographic image of iron-containing nanoparticles synthesized in uncompressed Langmuir monolayer (at $\pi = 0$) and deposited onto the mica substrate at $\pi = 25$ mN/m using vertical substrate lifting method. Conditions for nanoparticle synthesis: initial $Fe(CO)_5$/SA ratio was 10:1, UV exposure time 4 min, T = 294 K, subphase pH = 5.6. Image parameters: 580×580 nm^2, the black-to-white color height scale is 0-7 nm.

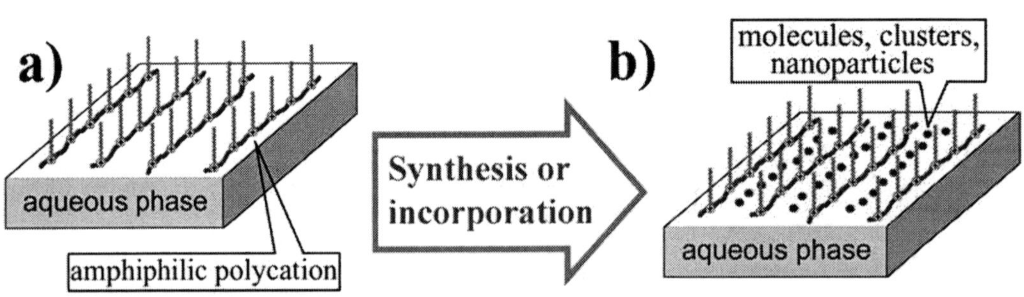

Figure 13. Schematic diagram of the polymeric nanoscale-organized planar monomolecular layer formed at the gas-liquid interface using amphiphilic polycation molecules (**a**), and corresponding nanoscale-ordered composite planar polymeric nanostructure with incorporated functional nanoscopic components – molecules, nanoclusters, nanoparticles, etc. (**b**)

Though it is not easy to form reproducibly 1-D chain structures from nanoparticles, however, this task was solved successfully by nature. Various magnetotactic bacteria can synthesize fine (40-100 nm) ferromagnetic crystalline iron oxide nanoparticles (Fe_3O_4 with a small admixture of γ-Fe_2O_3 phase) forming magnetosome structures in which membrane-bound magnetic nanoparticles are organized and arranged in regular chains [28, 29]. The chain magnetosome structures play important physiological role in bacteria giving them possibilities for orientation in the earth's magnetic field. There is an approach to formation of self-organized one-dimensional inorganic nanostructures (chains of nanoparticles and nanowires) based on the use of polymeric molecules (in particularly, DNA) as templates. 1-D metallic nanostructures (chains of Pt nanoparticles [30], silver [31] and gold [32] metallic nanowires), cadmium sulfide nanoparticles [33-35] and DNA–magnetite nanocomposite [36] were fabricated via DNA templating and stabilizing. We used novel ultrathin planar amphiphilic polycation complexes with DNA - monolayer and multilayer DNA/amphiphilic polycation complex LB films [37] as templates and nanoreactors for generation of inorganic nanostructures (semiconducting CdS and iron oxide nanoparticle quasi-linear arrays or aggregates). Figure 14 shows AFM top view topographic images of PVP-16 and complex DNA/PVP-16 LB films deposited onto the mica substrate (image 14a and images 14b-14d, correspondingly). Nanoscale-ordered planar structure of PVP-16 film is clearly seen from the image 14a). The characteristic morphologies of DNA/PVP-16 complexes which can be obtained in dependence on the amphiphilic polycation monolayer state during the DNA binding are presented on the Fig. 14b) (novel extended planar net-like structure) and Fig. 14d) (quasi-circular toroidal structure typical for compacted DNA). Individual DNA molecules also were observed (image 14c). The use of DNA/Fe^{3+}/PVP-16 complex films as precursors resulted in generation of chain-like arrays of small iron oxide nanoparticles (Fig. 15 a) and quasi-linear aggregated (Fig. 15b). Analogous effect was observed when semiconductor CdS nanoparticles were generated in DNA/Cd^{2+}/PVP-16 complex film (Fig. 15c and 15d). One can see that important feature of images with nanoparticles generated in DNA/PVP-16 complex film is the organized character of nanoparticles arrangement in the film. The data obtained illustrate the important role of DNA molecules in spatial organization of inorganic nanoparticles generated in DNA complexes what opens possibility for use of such complexes as templates and nanoreactors for fabrication of organized planar hybrid bio-organic - inorganic nanostructures. Aggregation and coalescence of adjacent nucleus and nanoparticles in linear structures of DNA complexes can result in formation of nanorods and nanowires (images 15b and 15d). The mean diameter of iron oxide nanoparticles generated in DNA/PVP-16 complex film was about 3 nm. Such small iron oxide nanoparticles may be perspective for nanoelectronic applications because single-electron tunneling effects can be observed in such nanoparticles at room temperature [38].

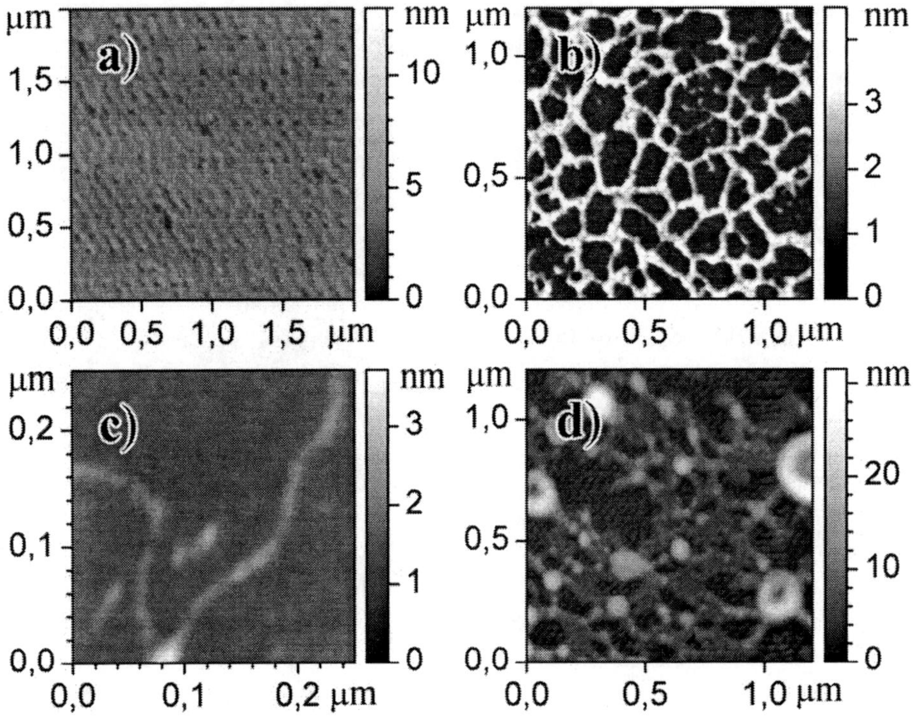

Figure 14. AFM tapping mode images of 2-layer LB films deposited onto the mica substrate. Image **a**): top view topographic image of PVP-16 LB film deposited after 10 min incubation of the PVP-16 Langmuir monolayer at low surface pressure value ($\pi \cong 0$) on the water subphase surface (pH=6) (image size 2 μm ×2μm, black-to-white color height scale is 0-13 nm). Image **b**): top view topographic images of DNA/PVP-16 complex LB film. Complex formation conditions: PVP-16 monolayer surface pressure value ~ 0 during the DNA binding, incubation time 25 min. The composition of the aqueous subphase was $1{,}2\times10^{-4}$ M DNA (for monomer), 1 mM NaCl, pH=6. (image size: 1.2 μm × 1.2 μm, black-to-white color height scale is 0-4.2 nm. Image **c**): single DNA molecule bound with PVP-16 monolayer, image size: 0.22 μm × 0.22 μm, black-to-white color height scale is 0-3.5 nm. Image **d**): top view topographic images of DNA/PVP-16 complex LB film. Complex formation conditions: PVP-16 monolayer surface pressure value 20 mN/m during the DNA binding, incubation time 25 min on the surface of aqueous subphase with composition: $1{,}2\times10^{-4}$ M DNA (for monomer), 1 mM NaCl, pH=6 (image size 1.2 μm × 1.2 μm, black-to-white color height scale is 0-30 nm).

Figure 16 demonstrates the possibilities of the other approach to formation of organized 1-D and 3-D bio-inorganic nanostructures. In that approach presynthesized nano-objects (cationic CdSe nanorods) were organized in crystalline structures via formation of complexes with DNA molecules. TEM micrographs showing organized crystalline complexes of DNA and CdSe nanorods formed via interaction of DNA/PVP-20 planar complexes with solution of functionalized cationic CdSe nanorods are presented on Figure 16. The highly anisotropic linear orientation of nanorods in the complex is clearly visible from images 16a) and 16b). Images 16c) and 16d) illustrate the different stages of formation of superstructures from DNA/CdSe nanorods complexes. Image a – Individual complexes (image 16 a) are pronounced highly anisotropic 1-D structures characterized by linear orientation of nanorods and parallel organization of nanorod filaments. Images 16b) and 16c) illustrate the different stages of formation of superstructures from DNA/CdSe nanorods complexes. Such complexes represent new class of nano-organized bio-inorganic nanostructures and can possess interesting anisotropic optical and electronic properties.

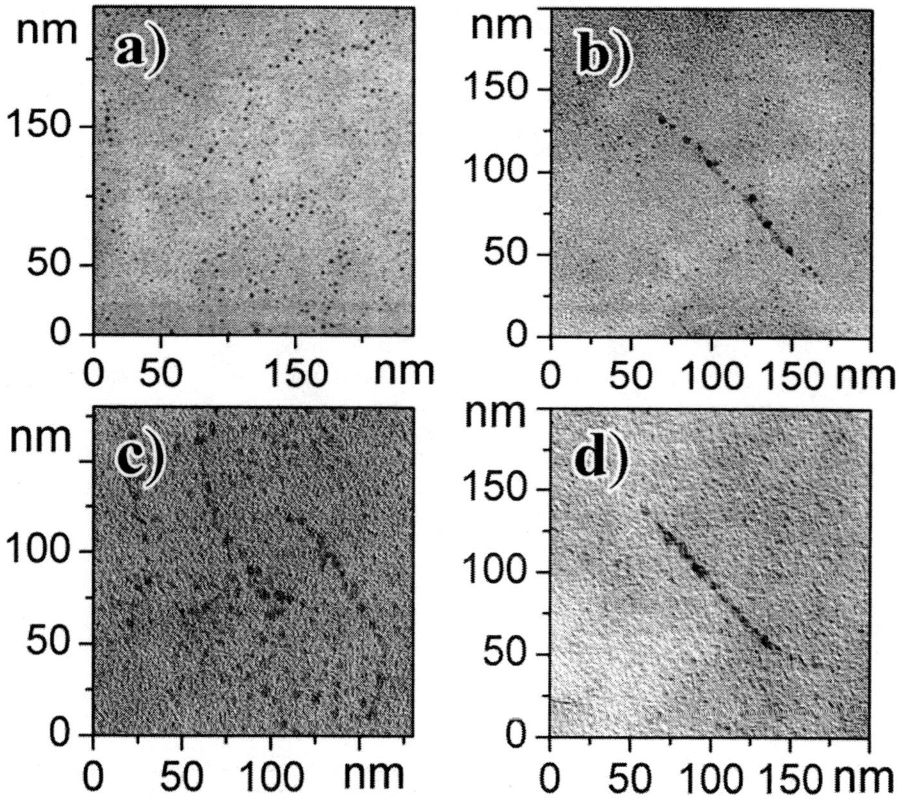

Figure 15. Transmission electron micrographs showing iron oxide and CdS nanoparticles and nanostructures grown in planar DNA/PVP-16 complex nanoreactors. Image **a**): Iron oxide nanoparticles grown in DNA/Fe^{3+}/PVP-16 complex LB film (incubation time 1 hour). Image **b**): Iron oxide nanowire grown in DNA/Fe^{3+}/PVP-16 complex LB film (incubation time 2 hours). Image **c**): CdS nanoparticles grown in DNA/Cd^{2+}/PVP-16 complex LB film. Image **d**): CdS nanowire grown in DNA/Cd^{2+}/PVP-16 complex LB film.

Figure 17 demonstrates fabrication of new nanocomposite nanostructures by the method of two-dimensional synthesis of inorganic nanoparticles in a monolayer at the gas-liquid interface [8] with amphiphilic polyelectrolytes used as surfactants to form organized Langmuir monolayer matrix and to stabilize grown nanoparticles. Iron oxide nanoparticles were grown in the monolayer formed by PVP-20. We have observed formation of organized chain-like arrays of those iron oxide nanoparticles (Fig. 17a). Figure 17b shows palladium nanoparticles generated in mixed Langmuir monolayer with polymeric surfactant. One can see the generation of small Pd nanoparticles (with main diameter about 3 nm) organized in quasi-linear arrays. Ligand exchange and substitution effects can be involved in the structure formation processes in the metal-organic precursor/PVP-20 monolayer. It is known that interaction of pyridine with tri-nuclear palladium acetate complex $Pd_3(CH_3COO)_6$ results in decomposition of the complex cycle with formation of mono-nucleus complex composed by Pd, acetate and pyridine ($Pd(Ac)_2[Py]_2$). Similar effects can take place when iron pentacarbonyl is present in the PVP-20 monolayer. The linear organization of Pd and iron atoms in such polymeric precursor complexes in the monolayer can be a reason for linear organization of corresponding interfacially grown Pd and iron oxide nanoparticles.The observed effects of amphiphilic polycation on the morphology of two-dimensionally grown nanoparticles can be also a result of specific complexing and stabilizing interactions of nucleus, growing nanoparticles and polymeric groups, along with of nonspecific electrostatic interactions of charged nanoparticles and amphiphilic polycation molecules.

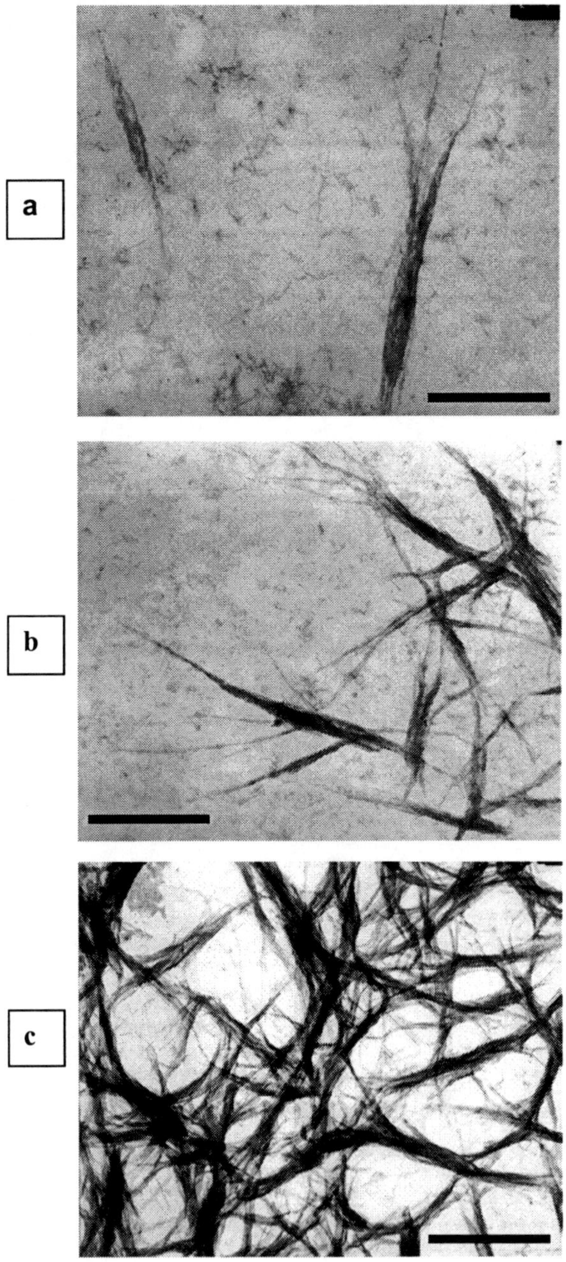

Figure 16. TEM micrographs showing organized crystalline complexes of DNA and CdSe nanorods formed via interaction of DNA/PVP-20 planar complexes with solution of functionalized cationic CdSe nanorods. Image **a**): black bar is 175 nm; Image **b**): black bar is 250 nm; Image **c**):black bar is 250 nm;

a

b

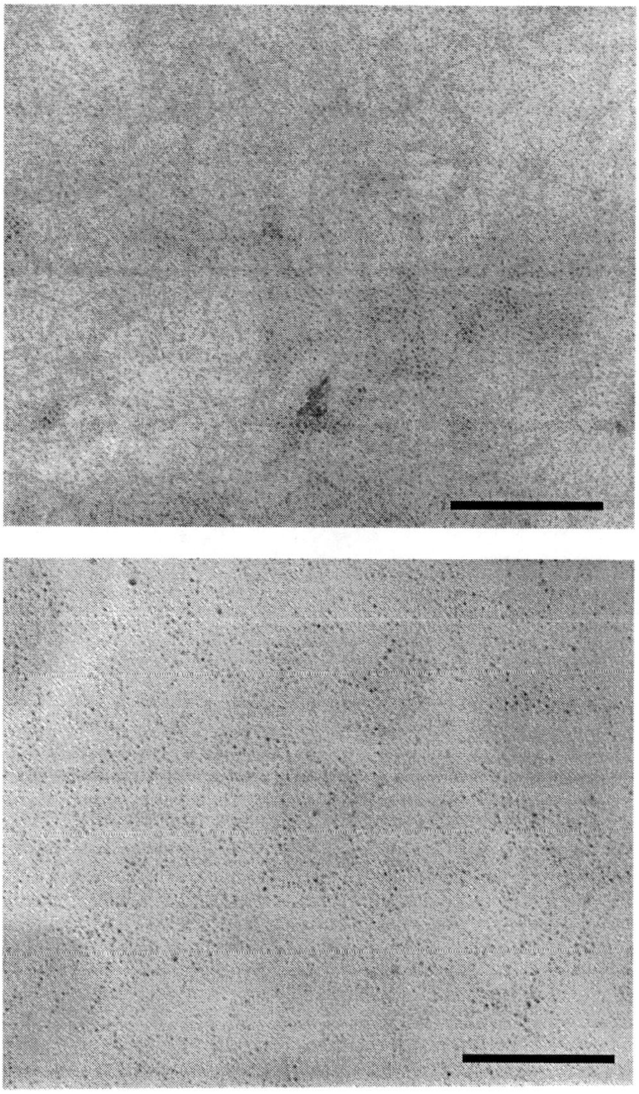

Figure 17. Transmission electron micrographs showing iron oxide and Pd nanoparticles interfacially grown in mixed PVP-20 monolayer. Image **a**): Iron-containing nanoparticles grown in monolayer with initial $Fe(CO)_5$/PVP monomer ratio 1:1, incubation time 60 min, black bar is 140 nm. Image **b**): Pd nanoparticles synthesized in monolayer with initial Pd_3Ac_6/PVP ratio 1:3, incubation time 60 min. Black bar is 140 nm.

4. CONCLUSIONS

A number of new synthetic and assembling nanofabrication methods based on the surface and interface interactions, biomimetic and bio-inspired strategies have been developed. The methods developed can be perspective for investigation of fundamental mechanisms of nano-scale structural organization and transformations in various molecular (including bio-molecular) structures, and for development of new low-dimensional bio-molecular and hybrid bio-organic-inorganic nanostructures, nanostructured films and coatings with advanced properties and potential for nanobiotechnological applications.

Acknowledgments

Some AFM images were gratefully obtained by Dr. R.V. Gainutdinov and Dr. A.L. Tolstikhina, Institute of Crystallography RAS (Moscow). STM measurements were carried out by Dr. A.S. Trifonov (MSU). I thank to Prof. S.P. Gibin, Prof. V.V. Kislov, Dr. E.S. Soldatov, Dr. Yu.A. Koksharov, Dr. M. Artemyev, Dr. A.Yu. Obydenov, Dr. A.S. Trifonov, Dr. T.V. Yurova, Ms. M.N. Antipina, Mr. A.N. Sergeev-Cherenkov for intensive and effective collaboration.

The work was supported by Russian Foundation for Basic Researches (Grant 02-03-33158), INTAS (Grant 99-864), ISTC (Grant 1991).

References

[1] R.B. Frankel, R.P. Blakemore (Eds): *Iron Biominerals*. Plenum Press, New York,1991.

[2] S. Mann: *Biomineralization: Principles and concepts in bioinorganic materials chemistry*. Oxford University Press, New York, 2001.

[3] X.K. Zhao, J. Yang, L.D. McCormick, J.H. Fendler: *J. Phys. Chem.*, **96**, 9933 (1992).

[4] S.P. Gubin: *Chemistry of clusters*. Nauka, Moscow, 1987.

[5] A.A. Yaroslavov, E.G. Yaroslavova, A.A. Rakhnyanskaya, F.M. Menger, V.A. Kabanov: *Colloid Surf. B*, **16**, 29 (1999).

[6] R.M. Fuoss, U.P. Strauss: *J. Polym. Sci.*, **3**, 246 (1948).

[7] G.B. Khomutov, S.A. Yakovenko, E.S. Soldatov, V.V. Khanin, M.D. Nedelcheva, T.V. Yurova: *Membr. Cell Biol.*, **10**, 665 (1997).

[8] G.B. Khomutov: *Colloids and Surfaces A*, **202**, 243 (2002).

[9] S. Roth, M. Burghard, G. Leising: *Curr. Opinion in Solid State & Mater. Sci.*, **3**, 209 (1998).

[10] S.P. Gubin, Yu.A. Gulayev, G.B. Khomutov, V.V. Kislov, V.V. Kolesov, E.S. Soldatov, K.S. Sulaimankulov, A.S. Trifonov: *Nanotechnology*, **13**, 185 (2002).

[11] A.P. Alivisatos: *Science*, **271**, 933 (1996).

[12] S. Datta: *Electronic Transport in Mesoscopic Systems*. Cambridge University Press, Cambridge, 1997.

[13] J.C. Huie: *Smart Mater. Struct.,* **12** 264 (2003).

[14] S. Boussaad, L. Dziri, R. Arechabaleta, N. J. Tao, R. M. Leblanc: *Langmuir*, **14**, 6215 (1998).

[15] S. Henrichs, C. P. Collier, R.J. Saykally, Y.R. Shen, J.R. Heath: *J.Am.Chem.Soc.,* **122** 4077, (2000).

[16] F.C. Meldrum, N.A. Kotov, J.H. Fendler: *J. Phys. Chem.*, **98**, 4506 (1994).

[17] G.B. Khomutov, L.V. Belovolova, S.P. Gubin, V.V. Khanin, A.Yu. Obydenov, A.N. Sergeev-Cherenkov, E.S. Soldatov, A.S. Trifonov: *Bioelectrochemistry*, **55**, 177 (2002).

[18] A.Yu. Obydenov, S.P. Gubin, V.V. Khanin, S.N. Polyakov, A.N. Sergeev-Cherenkov, E.S. Soldatov, A.S. Trifonov, G.B. Khomutov: *Colloid. Surf. A*, **198-200**, 389 (2002).

[19] G.B. Khomutov, V.V. Kislov, R.V. Gainutdinov, S.P. Gubin, A.Yu. Obydenov, S.A. Pavlov, A.N. Sergeev-Cherenkov, E.S. Soldatov, A.L. Tolstikhina, A.S. Trifonov: *Surf. Sci.*, 532–535, 287 (2003).

[20] D. Whang, S. Jin, Y. Wu, C.M. Lieber: *Nanoletters*, **3**, 1255 (2003).

[21] G.B. Khomutov, E.S. Soldatov, S.P. Gubin, S.A. Yakovenko, A.S. Trifonov, A.Yu. Obidenov, V.V. Khanin: *Thin Solid Films*, **327-329**, 550 (1998).

[22] A.A. Zubilov, S.P. Gubin, A.K. Korotkov, A.G. Nikolaev, E.S. Soldatov, V.V. Khanin, G.B. Khomutov, S.A. Yakovenko: *Tech. Phys. Lett.*, **20**, 195 (1994).

[23] S.A. Yakovenko, E.S. Soldatov, V.V. Khanin, A.S. Trifonov, S.P. Gubin, G.B. Khomutov: *Thin Solid Films*, **284-285**, 873 (1996).

[24] E.S. Soldatov, V.V. Khanin, A.S. Trifonov, S.P. Gubin, V.V. Kolesov, D.E. Presnov, S.A. Yakovenko, G.B. Khomutov: *JETP Letters*, **64**, 556 (1996).

[25] D. Porath, Y. Levi, M. Tarabiah, O. Millo: *Phys. Rev. D*, **56**(15), 9829 (1997).

[26] J. Zhu, A. Eisenberg, R.B. Lennox: *Macromolecules*, **25**, 6547 (1992).

[27] G.B. Khomutov, V.V. Kislov, M.N. Antipina, R.V. Gainutdinov, S.P. Gubin, A.Yu. Obydenov, S.A. Pavlov, A.A. Rakhnyanskaya, A.N. Sergeev-Cherenkov, E.S. Soldatov, D.B. Suyatin, A.L. Tolstikhina, A.S. Trifonov, T.V. Yurova: *Microelectronic Engineering*, **69**(2-4), 373 (2003).

[28] D. Schuler, R.B. Frankel: *Appl. Microbiol. Biotechnol.*, **52**, 464 (1999).

[29] R.B. Frankel, R.P. Blakemore, R.S. Wolfe: *Science*, **203**, 1355 (1979).

[30] M. Mertig, L.C. Ciacchi, R. Seidel, W. Pompe: *Nanoletters*, **2**, 841 (2002).

[31] J.J. Storhoff, C.A. Mirkin: *Chem. Rev.* **99**, 1849 (1999).

[32] O. Harnack, W.E. Ford, A. Yasuda, J.M. Wessels: *Nanoletters*, **2**, 919 (2002).

[33] J. L. Coffer, S. R. Bigham, R. F. Pinizzotto, H. Yang: *Nanotechnology*, **3**, 69 (1992).

[34] R. Mathab, J.P. Rogers, C.P. Singleton, C.J. Murphy: *J. Am. Chem. Soc.*, **117**, 7028 (1996).

[35] J.L. Coffer, S.R. Bigham, X. Li, R.F. Pinizzotto, Y.G. Rho, R.M. Pirtle, I.L. Pirtle: *Appl. Phys. Lett.,* **69** 3851 (1996).

[36] S. Mornet, A. Vekris, J. Bonnet, E. Duguet, F. Grasset, J.-H. Choy, J. Portier: *Materials Letters,* **42**, 183 (2000).

[37] M.N. Antıpına, R.V. Gainutdinov, A.A. Rachnyanskaya, A.L. Tolstikhina, T.V. Yurova, G.B. Khomutov: *Surf. Sci.,* **532–535**, 1025 (2003).

[38] R.G.C. Moore, S.D. Evans, T. Shen, C.E.C. Hodson: *Physica E*, **9**, 253 (2001).

In: Biocatalytic Technology and Nanotechnology
Editor: G. E. Zaikov, pp. 29-39
ISBN 1-59454-117-5

Chapter 2

INFLUENCE OF HUMIC SUBSTANCES ON DEGRADATION OF OIL BY OIL-OXIDIZING MICROORGANISMS

K. Salem[1], G. G. Mikailov[2], V. P. Murygina[2], I. V. Perminova[2], N. U. Grechicheva[1] and S. V. Mecheriakov[1]

1 I.M. Gubkin Russia State University, The industrial ecology department. 119991, Leninski str. 65, tel. (095)9395083, fax. (095)9395714,
2 Moscow State University, Chemical Faculty, Dept. of Chemical Enzymology, Leninskye Gory, Apt. 1/3, GCP-3, Moscow B-234, 119899, Russia
Fax: + 7(095) 939-5714, e-mail: vpm@enzyme.chem.msu.ru

ABSTRACT

This paper describes the results of investigation of the preparation "Rhoder" oil degradation activity in a model of oil-contaminated soil with 5% heavy oil (pre-heated oil under 272^0C) or soil of Balajary oil field, Resp. Azerbaijan (eight years old oil pollution, 180 g/kg dry soil) under laboratory conditions. This activity was compared with indigenous oil-degradation one with and without addition of Humic substanses (HS). Preparation "Rhoder"consists of two non-pathogenic oil degradaion bacterial strains (Rhodococcus ruber and Rhodoccus erythropolis). HS were presented by Sodium Humate (Irkutsk, IH), humic and gimatomelanic acids as well as Potassium Humate and Iron humate, obtained from IH and PowHumus in concentrations by 0,001, 0,01 and 0,1 %%. Preparation "Rhoder" decreased total hydrocarbon content of heavy oil by 24% and of Balajary field oil by 33%. HS increased an efficiency of heavy oil degradation with preparation "Rhoder" by 10-30%. The fermentation activity of oil polluted soil increased during bioremediation. Also it was shown that oil degradation activity of indigenous microorganisms in old oil pollution was comparable with preparation "Rhoder" activity. This fact confirms both our previously observed data and literary ones.

Key words: oil, pollution, oil-degradation microorganisms, preparation "Rhoder", humic substanses, bioremediation.

1. Introduction

Problem of environment protection from hydrocarbon pollution is a main problem in the world. Nowadays bioremediation methods are most perspective for this aim. They include both an activation of indigenous microorganisms and introduction of oil-oxidizing ones [1]. Addition of biologically active substances, for example, humic substances (HS), increases an efficiency of oil-polluted soil bioremediation [2]. HS have a complicated structure and are responsible for soil fertility [3]. In the recent time, HS are widely used for a detoxification of soil and water, polluted by heavy metals, radionuclides and also for bioremediation of chlorinated and organophosphorus pollutions. HS increase biodegradation availability of toxic compounds for microorganisms because HS are able to make complexes with toxic compounds [2].

According to the literature data, HS in low concentration (from 0,1 up to 0,9 g/l) have a promotional effect for microorganisms in oil-contaminated soils. In higher concentration (from 1 g/l up to 9 g/l) HS are used as fertilizers; in much higher concentration (from 10-60 g/l) - as sorbents [3].

Our preparation "Rhoder" tested in pilot and field experiments in 1998-2003 and showed decreasing of oil concentration in oil-contaminated soils in Moscow region, Western Siberia and Komi Republic during one warm season by 23-72% depending on initial oil concentration and weather conditions [4-6]. The preparation "Rhoder" (Certificate No 77.99.04.515Д.004855.08.01 issued by Russia Ministry of Health) consists of two Rhodococcus oil degradation strains and represents a concentrated suspension of live bacterial cells with 10^9 to 10^{10} cells/ml that are ready for the application without a preliminary activation [7]. The working suspension of "Rhoder" for treatment contains 10^6-10^7 oil degradation cells + Fertilizer (0.2% solution) $N_{60}:P_{60}:K_{90}$. This paper describes the results of investigation of HS influence on preparation "Rhoder" degradation activity in a model of oil-contaminated soil with 5% heavy oil or soil from Balajary oil field, Resp. Azerbaijan under laboratory conditions in comparison with indigenous ones.

2. Materials and Methods

In the experiments, there were used a model of soil (quartz sand, pH=6.9, size-0.63mkm) contaminated by heavy oil (5 % of pre-heated under 272^0C oil) and oil-contaminated soil, picked out from the Balajary oilfield, Azerbaijan (eight years old oil pollution, 180 g/kg dry soil). In one of the experimental variant, the oil-contaminated soil was diluted by pure quartz sand up to concentration of hydrocarbon (HC) about 30 g/kg of dry soil. Model of soil or soil (300 g) were put into plastic vessels (ϕ15 cm x 7 cm) and Humic substanses (HS) were added. HS were presented by Sodium Humate (Irkutsk, IH), humic and gimatomelanic acids as well as Potassium Humate and Iron Humate, obtained from IH and PowHumus (Germany). The concentrations of HS were 0,001, 0,01 and 0,1 %% in several variants of experiments. All experimental variants were four-fold repeated. Then, the vessels were placed into a hothouse with temperature 20-23^0C without natural light. The contaminated soils were treated three or four times by the suspension of "Rhoder" and fertilizers. The soil negative control variants were not treated with the preparation. The vessels were periodically watered and mixed to intensify oil degradation throughout experiments. The samples were taken for analyses before each treatment and 0.5 month after last treatment according to 5 points scheme [4,6]. In the same way, indigenous microorganisms were treated by fertilizers with or without addition of HS. The initial and residual THC and HC fractions were determined by gravimetric and column chromatography methods [8]. The initial THC was recognized as 100%.

Numbers of microorganisms in the treated soils were estimated by MPN method, using the meat-pepton agar for heterotrophic (ammonifying) bacteria (HT), Eshby-agar for olygotrophic (OT), and Raymond's liquid medium with oil for hydrocarbon-oxidizing bacteria (HCO) [9,10]. Soluble nitrogen and phosphorus in soil, humidity, pH and some soil enzymes activity were determined with standard agrochemical methods [11].

3. Results and Discussion

3.1. Laboratory Trials with Heavy Pre-Treated Oil

Preparation “Rhoder” was added four times in the experiments with HS influence on heavy oil degradation in model of contaminated soil (quartz sand).

All obtained results are presented in Fig. 1. Oil-oxidizing microorganisms of the preparation “Rhoder” dergaded heavy oil (pre-heated under 272^{0}C) by 24%. HS (particularly gimatomilanic acid) added to oil-ontaminated soil in concentration 0.1% (20 g/l) and humic acid-Fe in concentration 0.01% (2 g/l) increase oil degradation activity of the preparation “Rhoder” (Fig.1.). In a negative control (without preparation and HS treatment), there is no oil degradation during our experiments.

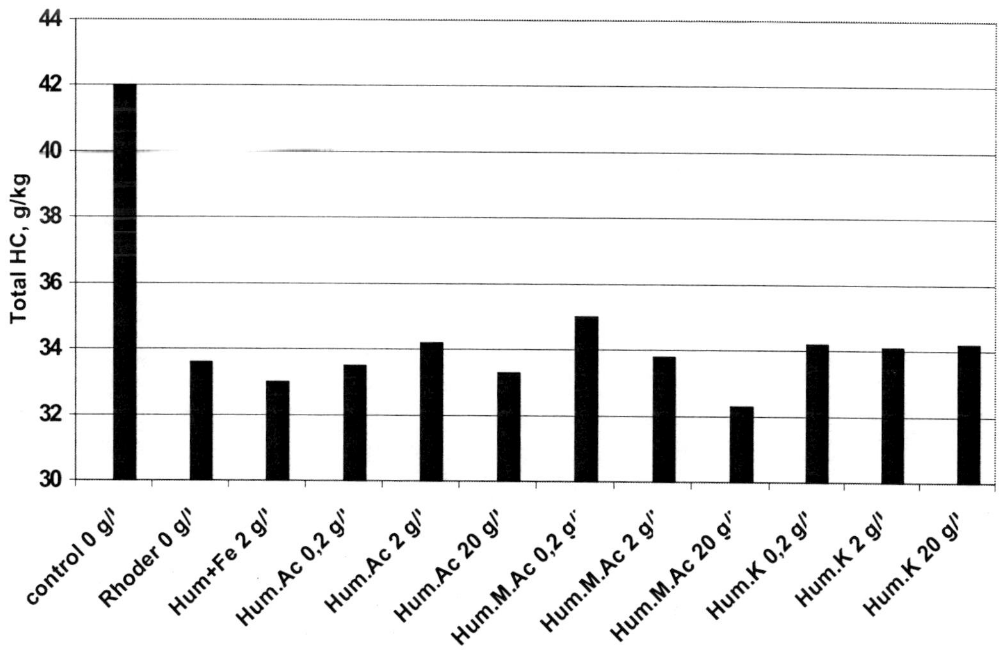

Fig.1. Influence of Humic Substances on oil degradation efficacy of preparation “Rhoder”

In all variants of experiments, positive influence of HS on oil degradation activity of the preparation "Rhoder" was demonstrated upon fractionation analysis of residual HC fractions. And this positive influence of HS depends on its concentration. So, IH (0.01% and 0.001%) and HA-Fe (0.001%) increase degradation of aliphatic hydrocarbons by 4-5 times in comparison without HS (only preparation "Rhoder"). HA (0.1%) and GMA (0.1% and 0.001%) and HA-Fe (0.1%) increase degradation of aromatic hydrocarbons by 2-3 times in comparison with the degradation by the preparation "Rhoder" without addition of HS [12].

3.2. Laboratory Trials with Oil Polluted Soil from Balajary Oilfield, Azerbaijan

Oil-polluted soil (Balajary oilfield, Azerbaijan) was treated three times with the preparation "Rhoder" in the oil degradation experiments with PowHumus as HS. Indigenous microorganisms were activated with fertilizers but without addition of preparation "Rhoder". The results of the preliminary examination of the oil-polluted soil are presented in Tables 1 and 2.

Table 1. Initial chemical and biological characteristics of the oil polluted soil (Balajary oilfield, Azerbaijan).

Samples	pH	Humi-dity %	THC, g/kg	Microorganisms, cells/g			$N\text{-}NH_4$, мg/100 g	$P\text{-}PO_4$ мg/100g
				HT	Oligotr.	HCO		
Pure Soil	7.7	1.4	3.1	2.8×10^6	3.9×10^6	1.0×10^4	0.34	8.3
Oil Polluted Soil	7.8	1.9	184.3	3.5×10^6	5.0×10^4	1.0×10^5	1.21	5.75
Sand+Oil Polluted Soil	7.7	1.8	32.1	1.9×10^5	1.7×10^4	1.0×10^3	1.63	4.06

Table 2. Enzymatic activity of the oil polluted soil (Balajary oilfield, Azerbaijan).

Samples	Catalase, ml 0.1 н $KMnO_4$/g dry soil/20 min	Polyphenoloxidase, ml purpuragallin/30 min/100 g soil	Dehydrogenaze, mg Threephenylfomazan/ g soil/day
Pure Soil	13.6	0.18	0.34
Oil Polluted Soil, 18%	12.8	13.03	4.53
Sand+Oil Polluted Soil, 3%	12.8	3.57	1.39

Obtained data show that highly oil-contaminated soil has slightly alkali pH (7,8); low content of ammonium nitrogen (1,21mg/100g of soil) and phosphate (5,75 mg/100g of soil). Total hydrocarbon content (THC) of soil is 184,3 g/kg of dry soil. There are many indigenous hydrocarbon-oxidizing microorganisms ($1{,}0 \times 10^5$ кl/g), including considerable amount of ammonifying and oligotrophic ones, which are evidence of active processes of natural self-remediation of soil as was shown through preliminary investigation of Balajary oilfield soil. The corresponding groups of microorganisms were ten times lower (Table 1) in pure and oil-contaminated soil diluted by pure quartz sand (model of soil). Ammonium nitrogen and phosphate in the model of soil were of small quantity, so it is necessary to add NPK fertilizers. Tested soils differ insignificantly one from another in terms of their enzymatic activity (Table 2). Thus, soil enzymatic activity of catalase is close to the absolute value, but polyphenoloxidase and dehydrogenase are two-fold values lower in the pure soil and 2-4 times higher in the oil-contaminated soils (18 %) in comparison with the soil diluted by sand (3%).

The decontamination dynamics of oil-polluted soils with the preparation "Rhoder" with and without HS (PowHumus 0.01%) are shown in Fig.2. It is seen that the oil degradation efficacy of indigenous microorganisms and preparation "Rhoder" ones differs very little at the end of the experiments: 11-19% and 14-17% (THC, 18%) and 18-24% and 23-24% (THC, 3%), respectively. The presence of HS has increased efficacy of degradation by 4-8% and 4-10% for two THC contents of oil-polluted soils, respectively.

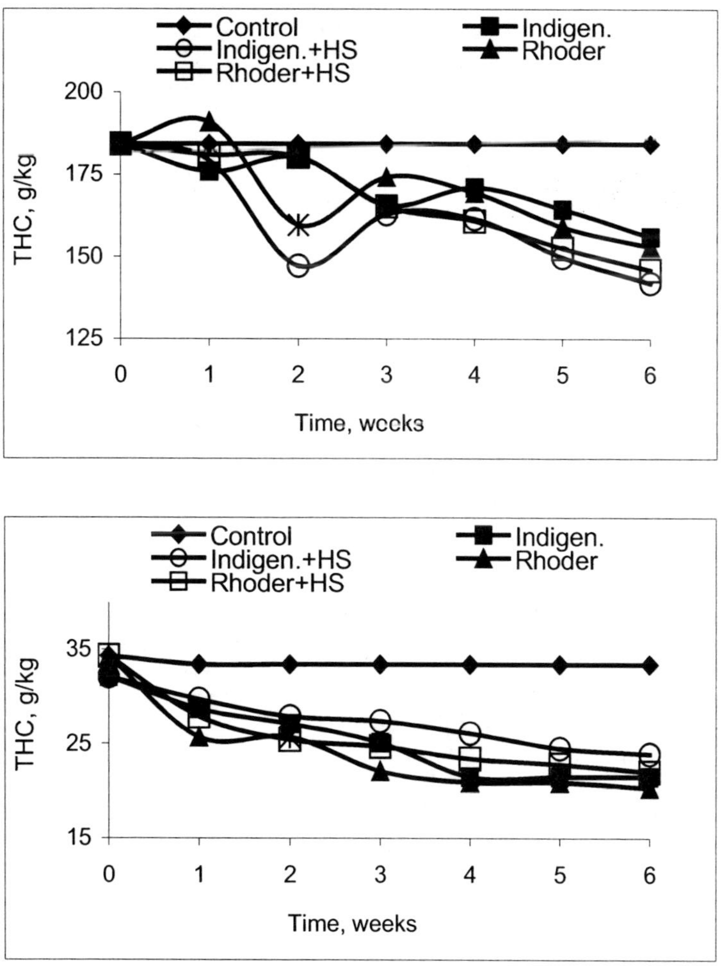

Fig. 2. Degradation of crude oil Baladjary oilfield, Azerbaijan with preparation "Rhoder" with and without HS.

The consumption of ammonium nitrogen and phosphates has been observed by 65-91% during the experiment and at the same time the stimulation effect of PowHumus on consumption of these fertilizers has not been observed.

In the course of bioremediation process, the number of different groups of microorganisms increased, first of all oligotrophic (OT), ammonifying (HT) and hydrocarbon-oxidizing bacteria (HCO), both upon activation of indigenous microorganisms and by introduction of the preparation "Rhoder" (Fig.3-5). It is well known that raising the number of different trophic groups of microorganisms is one of the most important restoration index of soil biological activity and at the same time it is an important efficacy index of bioremediation methods use [13].

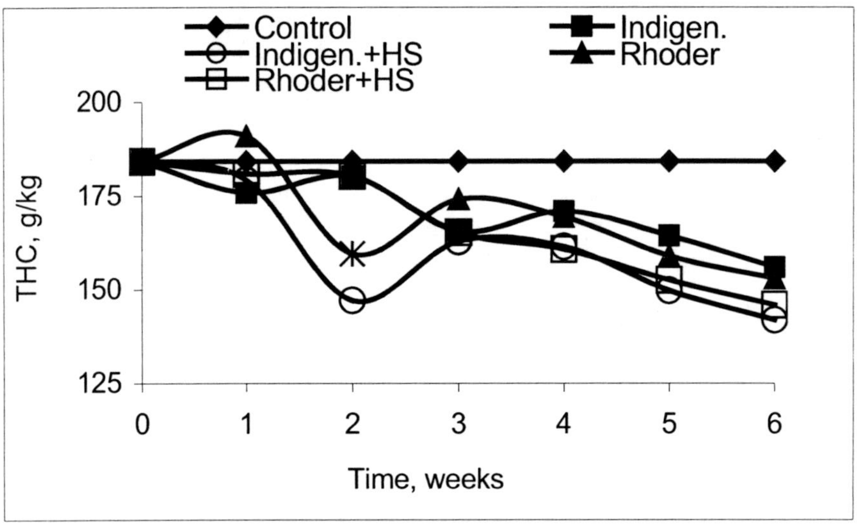

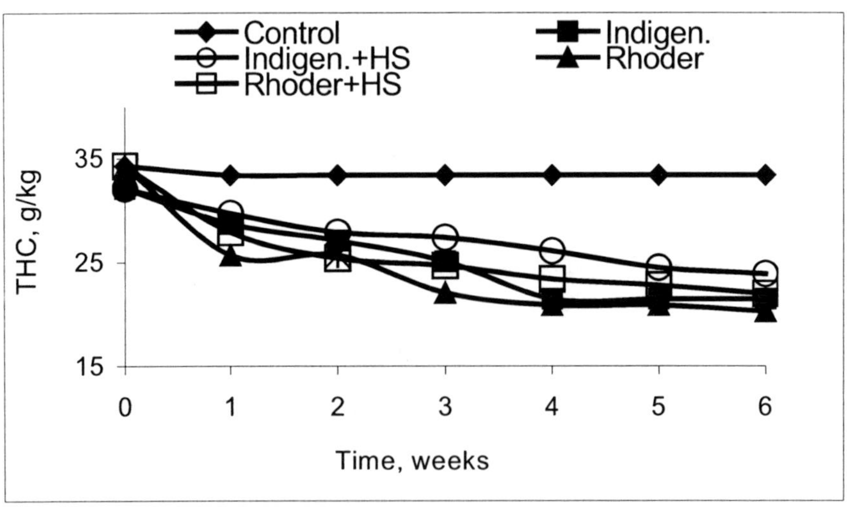

Fig. 3. Hydrocarbon degradation activity of the preparation "Rhoder" in comparison with indigenous microorganisms in oil polluted soil (Baladjary oilfield, Azerb. Repub.)

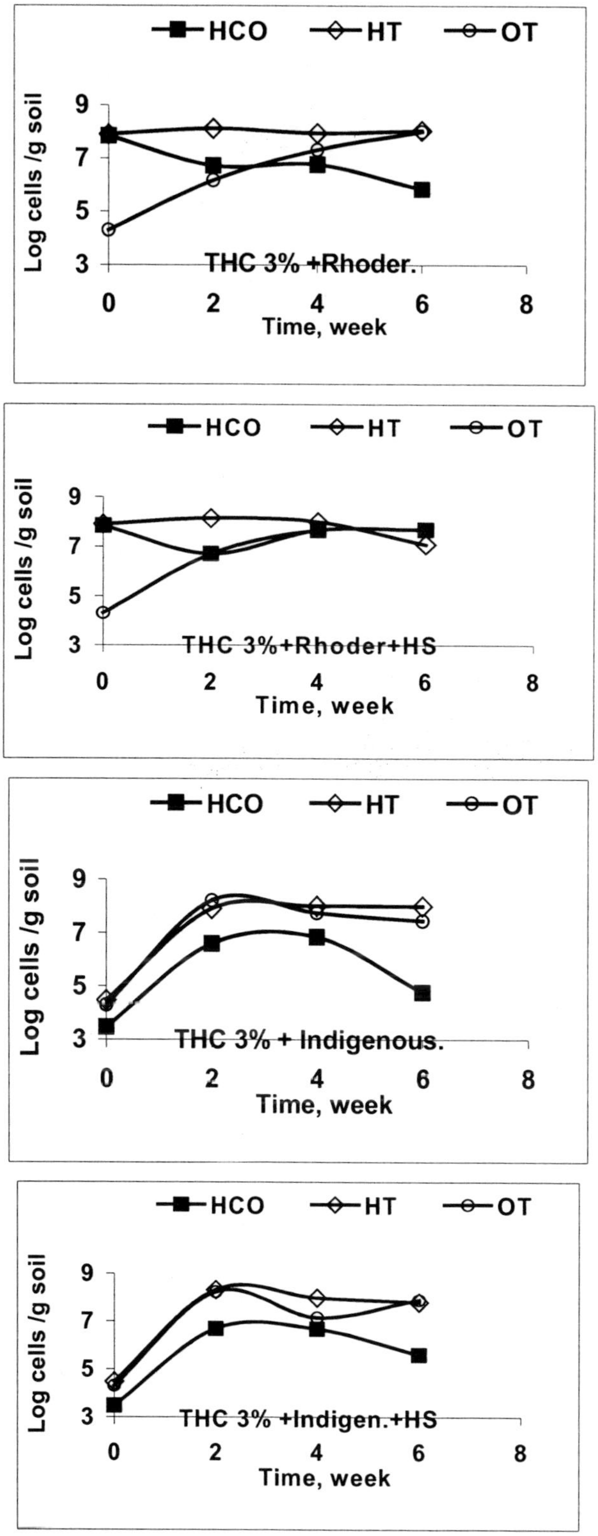

Fig. 4. Dynamics MPN of several trophic groups of bacteria during bioremediarion of oil polluted soil from Baladjary oilfield, Azerb. Repub.

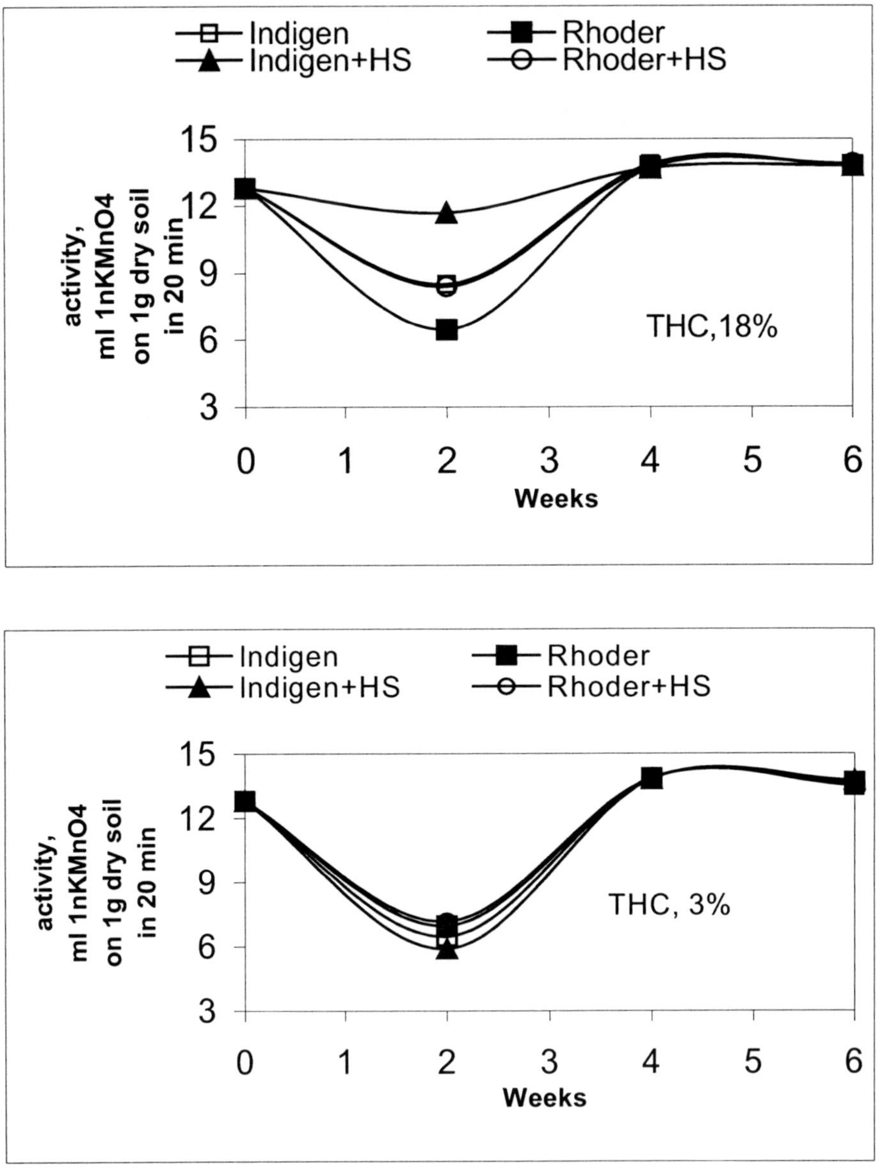

Fig. 5. Catalase activity of oil polluted soil during bioremediation with preparation «Rhoder» with and without HS in comparison with indigenous microorganisms.

Thus, the MPN of HT in oil-contaminated soil is always correlated with the MPN of HCO bacteria and increases while easily oxidizing HC are presented in soil, including water-soluble fractions of HC and the products of life activity of HCO microorganisms. Besides, MPN of HT bacteria is increasing in course of additions of ammonium nitrogen, which presents in the used fertilizers.

Oligotrophic microorganisms are highly sensitive to oil contamination and they are depressed greatly after accidental oil spills. At the stages of soil self-remediation, this group becomes active after removal of severe toxic effect of oil and that is just one of the main restoration indices of soil biological activity after oil pollution. Oil-oxidizing microorganisms (their number) are very important to decrease the concentration of HC in oil-polluted soil and show not only index of oil-oxidizing ability of soil but again the potential for its self-remediation [13].

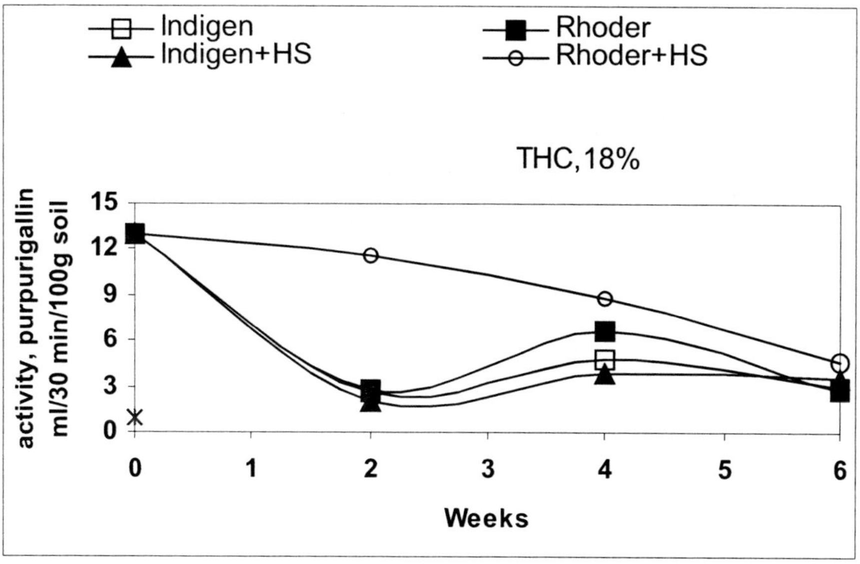

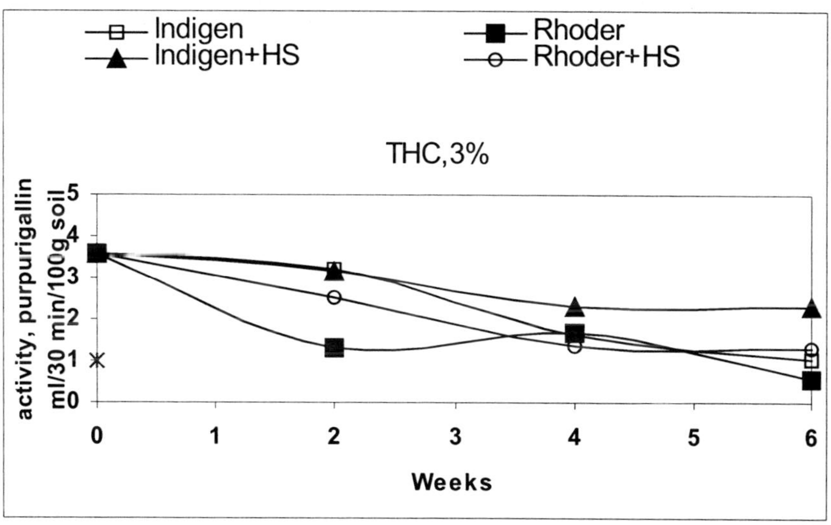

Fig. 6. Polyphenoloxidase activity of oil polluted soil during bioremediation with preparation «Rhoder» with and without HS in comparison with indigenous microorganisms.

The soil enzymatic activity is the most important one for evaluation of intensity of microbiological processes in it. Catalase, dehydrogenase and polyphenoloxidase activities of oil-polluted soil were evaluated. In course of bioremediation, it was observed that dehydrogenase activity of soil has increased (Fig.6). But catalase and polyphenolosidase activities decreased after the first treatment. It might have been caused by fertilizers addition and introduction of the preparation "Rhoder", as well as the increase of soil humidity and fluctuation of temperatures in a climatic compartment (Fig. 7). Further treatments with preparation have restored initial catalase and polyphenoloxidase activities and even increased it. A stimulation effect of PowHunus has not been revealed on numbers of various trophic groups of microorganisms and increasing of biological activity of the treated soils (Fig.6, 7). Our obtained results concerning the increase in the number of the main groups of microorganisms and soil biological activity, which are indices of the bioremediation processes of oil-contaminated soils, both upon activation of indigenous microorganisms and by introduction of the preparation "Rhoder" are in good conformity with the literature data [13]. Seeds of timothy-grass without their preliminary treatment by anti-stress agent were sowed after three-fold treatments of the oil contaminated soils with preparation "Rhoder". The experiment was stopped after three weeks because plants growth was not observed. The obtained results showed a high toxicity of the treated soils in closed systems (non-flow-through ditches with oil-contaminated soil). Grass grew only in the control clear sand and on soil, non-contaminated by oil. Positive impact of PowHumus on growth of the plants has not been revealed either.

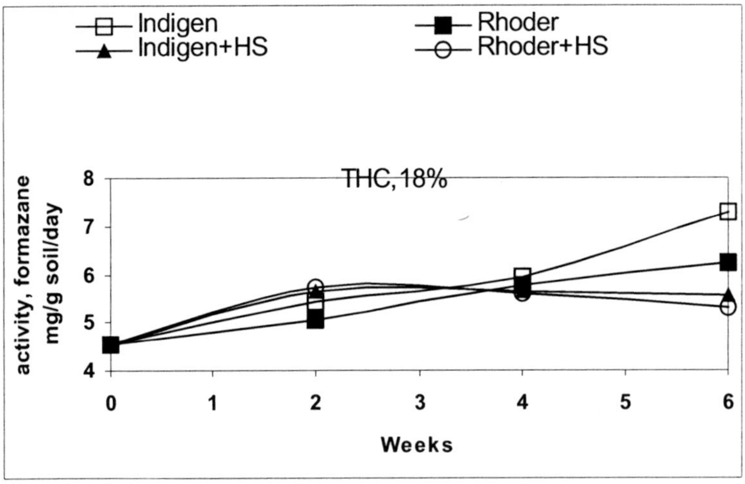

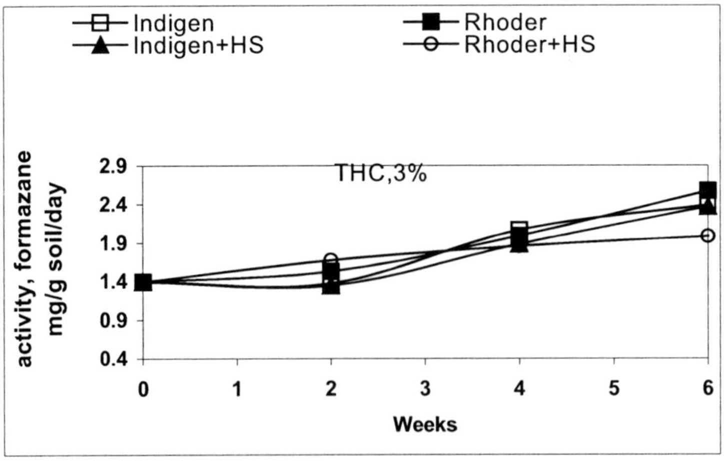

Fig. 7. Dehydrogenase activity of oil polluted soil during bioremediation with preparation «Rhoder» with and without HS in comparison with indigenous microorganisms.

4. CONCLUSIONS

The executed trials show that the preparation "Rhoder" decreases total hydrocarbon content of heavy oil by 24% and by 33% of Balajary field oil (Azerbaijan). The humic substances make a positive effect on biodegradation of heavy oil, increasing effectiveness of the preparation "Rhoder" by 10-30% and by 2-5 times increasing degradation of aromatic and aliphatic hidrocarbons of heavy oil, accordingly. During bioremediation the biological activity of the soil is increased, that means increasing of soil enzymatic activities and MPN of some trophic groups of microorganisms by 1.5-2 times. In old oil contamination (Balajary field oil, Azerbaijan) the degradation activity of indigenous microorganisms is compared to the activity of the preparation "Rhoder", which is in accordance with the experience accumulated by us and the literary data.

REFERENCES

[1] L. Ronald, Don L. Crawford. *Bioremediation: Principles and Applications*, Cambridge University Press (1996).

[2] V. Kholodov, N. Kulikova, I. Perminova: *Proc. of NATO Advanced Research Workshop.* September 23-29, Zvenigorod, Russia, 22 (2002).

[3] D.S.Orlov Humic substabses in biosphere. Moscow, *Science*, 16 (1993) (in Russian)

[4] V.P. Murygina, M.U. Arinbasarov, S.V. Kalyuzhnyi: *Biodegradation*, 11 (6), 385 (2000).

[5] V.P. Mouryguina, S.V. Kalyuzhny: *Proc. of the First European Bioremediation Conference*, 3-5 June, Crete, Greece, 28 (2001).

[6] V.P. Murygina, S.V. Kalyuzhnyi, M.U.Arinbasarov: *Proc. Intern. Confer. of ICS and UNIDO "New Technologies for Clean up Oil Contaminated Waters and Soils, remaking and use Oil-Slimes".*, 10-11 of December, Moscow, 27 (2001) (in Russian).

[7] V.P. Murygina, N.E. Voishvillo, S.V. Kalyuzhnyi *Patent RF No 2174496* (in Russian)

[8] Ed. E. Bogomolov *Modern methods of oil analysis,* M., the Higher School, 341 p. (1984) (in Russian).

[9] T. Nazina, Ye. Rozanova, S. Belyayev, M. Ivanov: "*Chemical and microbiological methods of investigation of liquid and solid samples from oil fields*". Biological Center Press, Pushchino, 35 p. (1988) (in Russian).

[10] Ed. F. Gerhardt in *Methods of common bacteriology,* (1984) (in Russian).

[11] E. Durynina, V. Egoroff: *Agrochemical analysis of soil, plants, fertilizer.* MSU Moscow, 147 p. (1998) (in Russian).

[12] K.M. Salem, I.V. Perminova, N.Ju. Grechischeva, V.P. Mouryguina, S.V. Mescheryakov: *Ecology and Industry*, April, 19, (2003) (in Russian).

[13] M. Markarova, L.G. Emelyanov: *Proc. Confer. Actual problems of biology.* April 14-16, Siktivkar, Russia, 135, (1999) (in Russian).

In: Biocatalytic Technology and Nanotechnology
Editor: G. E. Zaikov, pp. 41-50
ISBN 1-59454-117-5

Chapter 3

DEGRADATION OF AZO DYES BY METHANOGENIC SLUDGE

N. A. Yemashova[1], A. F. Telegina[2], I. B. Kotova[2] and S. V. Kalyuzhnyi[1]

[1] Chemical Enzymology Department, Chemistry Faculty, The Lomonosov Moscow State University (MSU), 119992, Vorobiovy Gory, 1/11, Moscow, Russia; Phone: (095) 939-5083; Fax: (095) 939-5417; E-mail: svk@enz.chem.msu.ru; URL: http://www.enzyme.chem.msu.ru/ekbio/eng/index.html

[2] Microbiology Department, Biology Faculty, The Lomonosov Moscow State University (MSU), 119992, Vorobiovy Gory, Moscow, Russia; Phone: (095) 939-5483

ABSTRACT

The toxicity potential and decolourisation of 3 acid azo dyes (Acid Orange 6, Acid Orange 7 and Acid Orange 52) by methanogenic granular sludge from anaerobic EGSB reactor was assayed. Complete bioreduction was found for all azo dyes under investigation. Sulphanilic acid and 4-aminoresorcinol were detected from the decolourisation of Acid Orange 6; sulphanilic acid and 1-amino-2-naphtol were detected from the reduction of Acid Orange 7 and also sulphanilic acid and N,N-dimethyl-1,4-phenylenediamine were found to be the intermediates of Orange 52 degradation. Sulphanilic acid and 1-amino-2-naphtol are resistant in the anaerobic conditions. On the contrary, 4-aminoresorcinol was completely mineralised by anaerobic sludge and N,N-dimethyl-1,4-phenylenediamine transformed into 1,4-phenilendiamine. Since anaerobic sludge contains sulphate-reducing bacteria and therefore it may generate sulphide, azo dyes were tested for chemical decolourisation by sulphide to compare rates of chemical and biological reduction.

Key words: Azo dyes, methanogenic sludge, toxicity, bioreduction, chemical reduction.

INTRODUCTION

Azo dyes represent a class of complex aromatics containing one or more azo groups. Azo dyes are widely used in textile and other industries (McMullan et.al., 2001; Manu and Chaudhari, 2002). All azo dyes currently used are synthetic compounds and xenobiotics. The presence of these aromatics may create serious environmental problem. Furthermore, the products of their transformation – aromatic amines – possess mutagenic or carcinogenic activities for living cells (Donlon et. al., 1997). Researches associated with the development of dye treatment technology are topical now (Slokar and Marechal, 1998; Robinson et. al., 2001). The majority of azo dyes are readily transformed by anaerobic microorganisms due to splitting the azo bond to form aromatic amines. The aromatic amines are colourless, so the azo bond cleavage represents a decolourisation process (Tan, 2001). The next step of the azo dye degradation is the conversion of aromatic amines. Mineralisation of aromatic amines in aerobic conditions is a common process. Yet, note that some aromatic amines are readily autooxidised in presence of oxygen to oligomeric and polymeric substances. On the other hand, anaerobic bacteria can degrade same aromatic amines characterized by presence of hydroxyl and carboxyl groups (Razo-Flores, 1997; Kalyuzhnyi et.al., 2000).

The goal of this paper was to investigate toxicity for methanogens and biodegradability of 3 widely used acid azo dyes in presence of methanogenic granular sludge. The biological azo dye reduction rate was evaluated and compared with the rate of chemical reduction by sulphide.

MATERIALS AND METHODS

Biomass and Basal Medium

Methanogenic granular sludge from an EGSB reactor treating brewery wastewater (Efes-Moscow) was used in our experiments.

The basal medium in all batch experiments contained (mg l^{-1}): $NaHCO_3$ (5000), NH_4Cl (280), $CaCl_2{\cdot}2H_2O$ (10), K_2HPO_4 (250), $MgSO_4{\cdot}7H_2O$ (100), yeast extract (100), H_3BO_3 (0.05), $FeCl_3{\cdot}4H_2O$ (2), $ZnCl_2$ (0.05), $MnCl_2{\cdot}4H_2O$ (0.05), $CuCl_2{\cdot}2H_2O$ (0.03), $(NH_4)_2SeO_3{\cdot}5H_2O$ (0.05), $AlCl_3{\cdot}6H_2O$ (2), $NiCl_2{\cdot}6H_2O$ (0.05), $Na_2SeO_3{\cdot}5H_2O$ (0.1), EDTA (1), and 36% HCl; pH 7.

Assays

The toxicities of the azo dyes used at the concentrations 0.5, 1, 2, 3 and 4 mM were determined using aceticlastic methanogenic activity assay (Razo-Flores, 1997). These assays were performed in 120 ml glass serum vials closed with a butyl rubber septum and an aluminium cap. The bottles containing 50 ml of the basal medium were flushed with argon. Then the aqueous solution of investigated dyes and the granular sludge (1.0 g VSS l^{-1}) were added. Acetate (0.5 ml) was added from 2.85 M sodium acetate solution. The assay bottles were incubated at 30°C. The CH_4 concentration and pressure in the headspace of the serum flasks were recorded throughout the incubation, and the specific aceticlastic activities of the sludge were calculated from a linear segment of kinetic curves of methane production. The aceticlastic activity of the sludge not treated with a toxicant was taken as control. From the concentration dependences of the specific activities, the 50% inhibiting concentration (IC_{50}) values for the azo dyes were estimated.

Azo dye reduction experiments were performed in 120 ml serum bottles. These bottles were filled with 50 ml of basal medium, granular sludge (1.0 g VSS l^{-1}), and 1 mM Acid Orange 6 or Acid Orange 7, or 0.2 mM Acid Orange 52. Then, they were closed with the butyl rubber septum and the aluminium cap. The headspace of the bottles was flushed with argon. The assays were performed in duplicate. Likewise, the experiment in presence of 1 mM ethanol, as external electron donor, was carried out. The assay bottles were incubated at 30°C. The concentrations of methane and co-substrate were measured gas chromatographically and the dye concentrations spectrophotometrically. For this purpose, the samples were centrifuged and diluted with phosphate buffer (1 M, pH 7) in the 1:20 ratio.

The chemical azo dye reduction assays were performed identically with the biological assays excepting that sulphide was added to the final concentration 5, 0.5 or 0.05 mM in place of the granular sludge. The concentrations of dyes were 0.5, 0.25 or 0.025 mM, respectively.

Chemicals

All chemicals were purchased from Acros (USA) and were of the highest purity commercially available and were not further purified.

Analyses

The methane and carbon dioxide contents in the headspace of the serum flasks were determined on a gas chromatograph LHM 8MD (Russia) equipped with a steel column (2m) packed with Porapak QS. The temperature of the column, injector port and conductivity detector was 50°C. Argon was used as carrier gas with a flow rate of 30 ml·min^{-1}. The gas sample volume was 200 μl.

Volatile fatty acids (VFA) and alcohols were detected on a gas chromatograph Chrom-5 (Czechoslovakia) equipped with a glass column (1m) packed with Chromsorb 101. The temperatures of the column, injector port and flame ionisation detector were 190, 200 and 200°C, respectively. Argon was used as carrier gas with a flow rate of 30 ml·min^{-1}. The aqueous sample volume was 1 μl.

The azo dye concentrations were measured spectrophotometrically with a Shimadzu UV-1202 spectrophotometer (Japan) at the absorbance maxima 428 nm (Acid Orange 6), 490 nm (Acid Orange 7) and 465 nm (Acid Orange 52). Samples were centrifuged, then, the aliquots (100μl) were diluted in 2 ml 0.1 M phosphate buffer (pH 7.0) solution and measured in a 1.0 cm quartz cuvette.

The aromatic amines formed were analysed on a high performance liquid chromatography (HPLC). Reverse phase column was packed with a Diasorb 130-C_{16}T, 6 μm. The chromatograph (Gilson, Germany) was equipped with a UV detector. Methanol with 1% acetic acid was used as liquid phase with a flow rate of 1 mL·min^{-1}. The pressure was 14 Mpa and the aqueous sample volume was 10 μl.

Results and Discussion

Toxicity of Azo Dyes

The literature describing toxicity of azo dyes for anaerobic microorganisms is substantial (Razo-Flores, 1997; Kalyuzhnyi and Sklyar, 2000). Sulphonated azo dyes are often more toxic for anaerobic microorganisms than the corresponding unsulphonated compounds (Tan, 2001). Note that from all classes of organisms participating in anaerobic biodegradation, methanogens are the slowest growing organisms, so that the toxic compound may strongly influence them. Thus, the toxicities of Acid Orange 6, Acid Orange 7 and Acid Orange 52 were assayed with regard to aceticlastic methanogenic activity of anaerobic sludge (Fig. 1). Figure 1 shows that Acid Orange 6 is less toxic for methanogens than Acid Orange 7 and Acid Orange 52 (50% inhibiting concentrations were found to be 2.50, 0.90 and 0.25 mM for Acid Orange 6, Acid Orange 7 and Acid Orange 52, respectively). Methanogenic activity increased up to 2.00 mM of Acid Orange 6. This is explicable by degradation of 4-aminoresorcinol (breakdown product of this dye) generating acetate as intermediate.

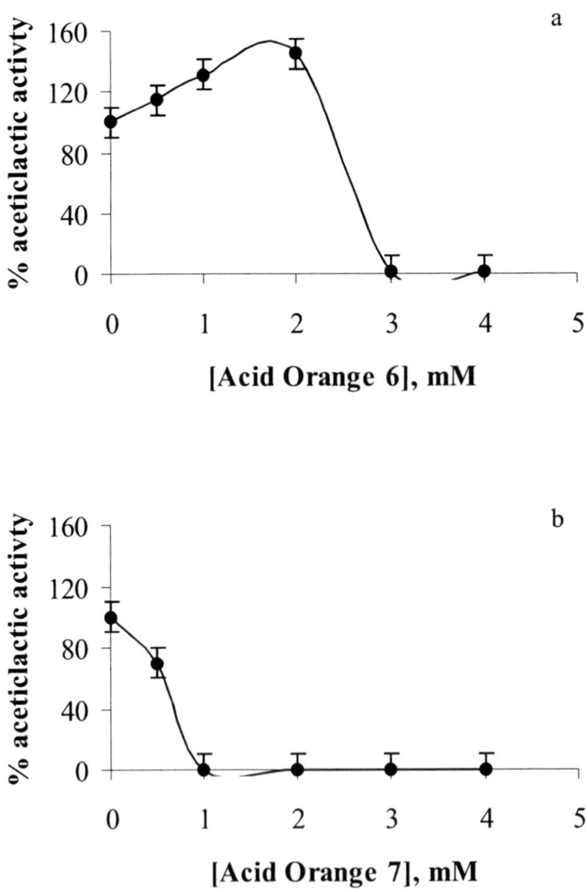

Figure 1. continued on next page.

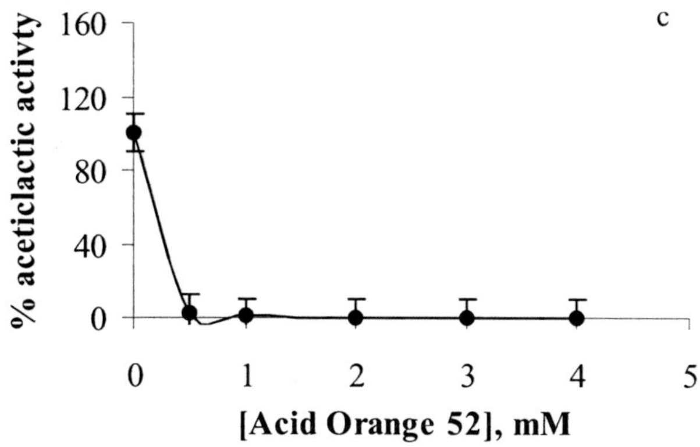

Fig. 1 (continued). Influence of concentrations of tested azo dyes (a – Acid Orange 6, b – Acid Orange 7, c – Acid Orange 52) on anaerobic sludge aceticlastic methanogenic activity.

Biodegradation of Azo Dyes

All the azo dyes tested were found to be completely decolourised (Fig. 2). The colour was eliminated due to cleavage of the azo bond. In all cases, the reaction products were colourless. Addition of ethanol as donor of reductive equivalent for splitting the azo bond did not accelerate decolouration of azo dyes. The fact that anaerobic sludge can easily degrade various azo dyes points to the non-specific character of this process. The azo bond bioreduction proceeded with no lag period and followed the first-order kinetics with respect to dye concentration (1).

$$C = C_0 \times e^{-kt}, \quad (1)$$

where C is the current concentration of azo dye at the given time (M), Co is the initial concentration (M), t is the time (days), k is the kinetic (first-order) constant (day^{-1}).

Kinetic constants were calculated from the time course of azo dyes concentration. The determined values of these constants are 0.20±0.02, 0.30±0.03 and 0.49±0.03 days $^{-1}$ for Acid Orange 6, Acid Orange 7 and Acid Orange 52, respectively. These data are at variance with azo dyes toxicities. Despite the high toxicity of Acid Orange 52 the rate of its reduction was highest. Note that the methanogens with determined toxicities are not involved in the azo dye decomposition. Likewise, the rate of azo dye reduction is a function of their chemical structure, while the toxicity can be related to cell membrane disruption.

The reduction of azo dyes was mediated biologically since assays in absence of sludge and in presence of autoclaved sludge (killed cells) showed no any decolourisation of azo dyes.

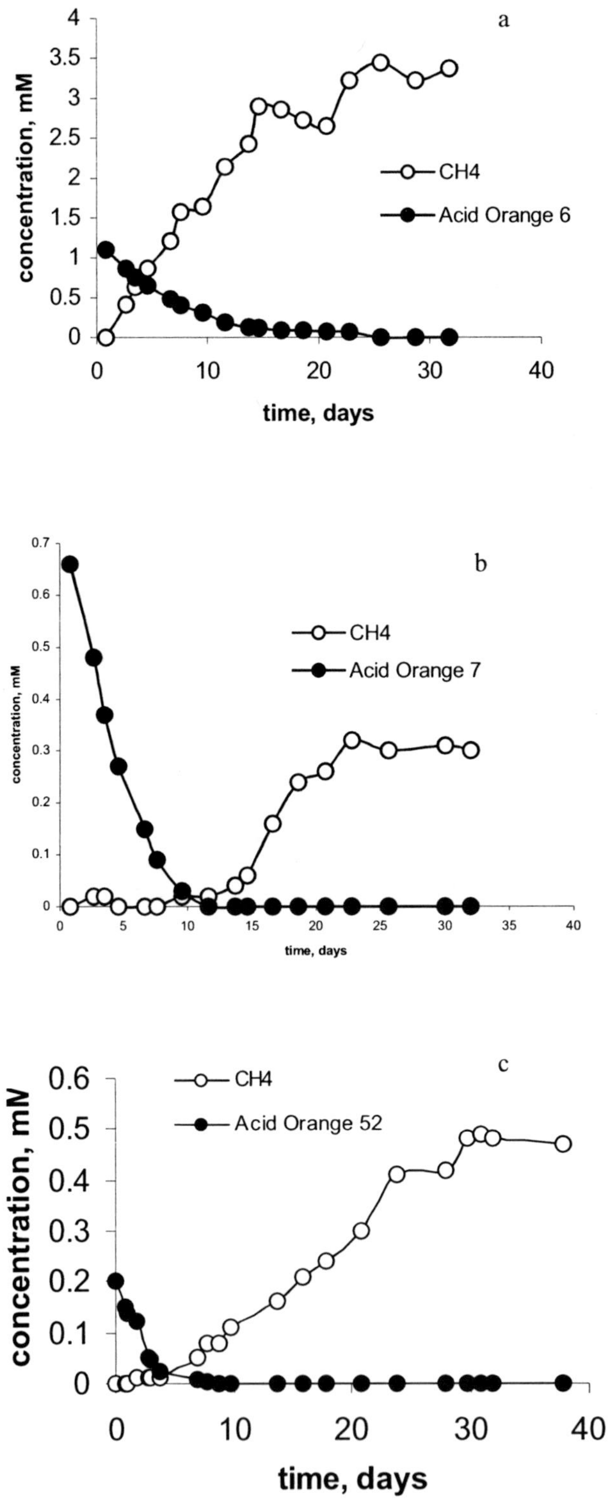

Fig.2. Bioconversion of azo dyes (a – Acid Orange 6, b – Acid Orange 7, c – Acid Orange 52) in the anaerobic environments.

During Acid Orange 6 decolourisation, gradual methane accumulation was observed. This fact manifested the mineralisation of breakdown products of the azo dye. Two aromatic amines appeared as intermediates of Acid Orange 6 reduction (sulphanilic acid and 4-aminoresorcinol (2)):

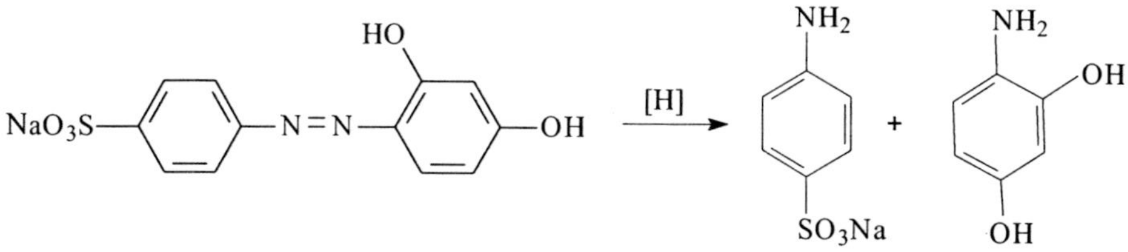

(2)

Sulphanilic acid is known to be resistant to biodegradation in anaerobic environments (Tan, 2001). HPLC method showed the remaining sulphanilic acid concentration to be fairly constant. The other product of Acid Orange 6 degradation (4-aminoresorcinol) seems to be mineralised by sludge. Theoretically, the amount of methane produced, resulting from 4-aminoresorcinol mineralisation, is 3 times more then the initial concentration of 4-aminoresorcinol (in mM). This was proven experimentally (Fig 2a).

Sulphanilic acid and 1-amino-2-naphtol were detected from the reduction of Acid Orange 7 (3).

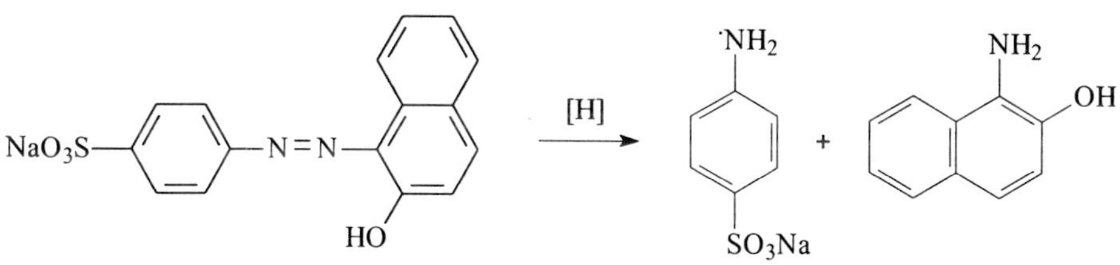

(3)

Both substances are resistant in anaerobic conditions (Tan, 2001; Zee, 2002). Low methane production was detectable during the incubation period for as long as a month (Fig. 2b). This means that sulphanilic acid and 1-amino-2-naphtol were not mineralised by the sludge.

Acid Orange 52 was also completely decolourised by methanogenic sludge. Two aromatic amines were determined after dye reduction - sulphanilic acid and N,N-dimethyl-1,4-phenylenediamine (DMP) (4).

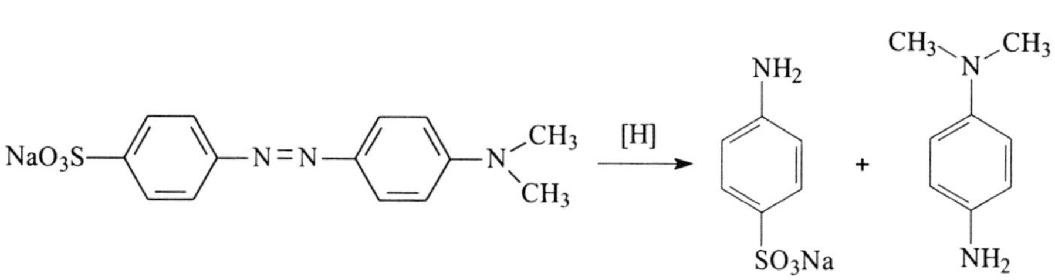

(4)

Immediately after the azo dye has been decolourised, methane production increased (Fig. 2c). This can be attributed to demethylations of DMP and 1,4-phenilenediamine formations as confirmed by HPLC. Theoretically, two molecules of methane appear from DMP conversion, and this fact was proven experimentally. On the contrary, 1,4-phenilenediamine was resistant to further degradation.

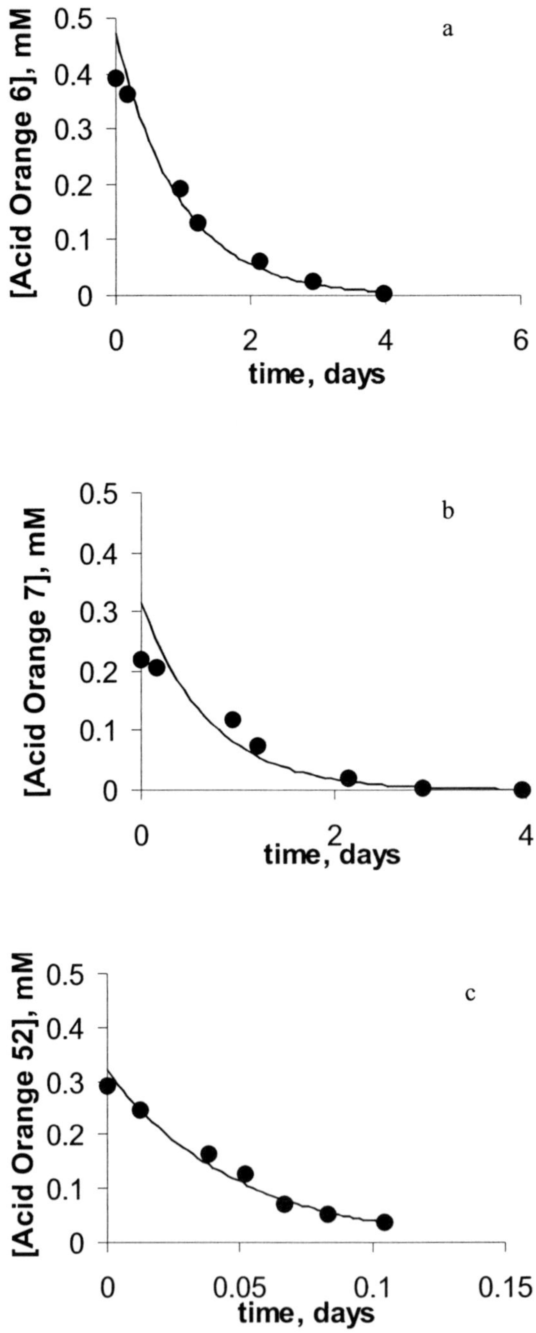

Fig. 3. Decolourisation of tested azo dyes (a – Acid Orange 6, b – Acid Orange 7, c – Acid Orange 52) by sulphide (initial sulphide concentration 5 mM).

Reduction of Azo Dyes by Sulphide

Anaerobic granular sludge usually contains sulphate reducing bacteria. Therefore, sulphide can be present in the sludge and may facilitate the azo dye reduction. Thus, the azo dye decolourisation was studied without sludge but at the sulphide concentrations 0.05 mM, 0.5 mM and 5 mM. Figure 3 shows that all dyes under research were reduced by sulphide. The products in all cases were the same as for bioreduction. The azo dyes reduction rates and sulphide concentrations showed linear relationship, i.e., the reduction accelerated with the increase in sulphide concentration. Chemical azo dyes reduction also followed the first-order kinetics with respect to dye concentration. But in contrast to biological decolourisation, the lag period was observed in the beginning of reduction by sulphide, especially at low sulphide concentrations. This fact may be related to sulphide reaction and the remaining oxygen in the medium. For all sulphide concentrations, Acid Orange 52 showed the highest value of kinetic constant while Acid Orange 6 the lowest one, like for biodegradation (Table 1). This confirms the fact that the azo dye reduction rate, biological or chemical, is dependent on the chemical structure of substrate.

Table 1. First-order rate constants values for azo dye decolourisation by sulphide.

Sulphide, mM	5	0.5	0.05
k (Acid Orange 6), day^{-1}	1.07	0.10	0.06
k (Acid Orange 7), day^{-1}	1.44	0.40	0.29
k (Acid Orange 52), day^{-1}	20.86	0.88	0.20

CONCLUSIONS

The following conclusions can be drawn from the research described.

1. Toxicities of 3 azo dyes (Acid Orange 6, Acid Orange 7 and Acid Orange 52) were determined with regard to aceticlastic methanogenic activity of anaerobic sludge. Acid Orange 6 is less toxic for methanogens than Acid Orange 7 and Acid Orange 52.
2. All the azo dyes tested were completely decolourised by metanogenic anaerobic sludge. The first-order kinetics described the azo dyes reduction. Sulphanilic acid and 4-aminoresorcinol have been detected from decolourisation of Acid Orange 6. Sulphanilic acid and 1-amino-2-naphtol have been detected from the reduction of Acid Orange 7. Likewise, sulphanilic acid and DMP have been found to be intermediates of Orange 52 degradation. Sulphanilic acid and 1-amino-2-naphtol are resistant in anaerobic conditions, 4-aminoresorcinol has been completely mineralised by anaerobic sludge. DMP has been transformed into 1,4-phenilendiamine.
3. The azo dyes reduction by sulphide at the concentrations 5, 0.5 and 0.05 mM was investigated. The lag period observed in the beginning of reaction between azo dyes and sulphide can be related to the reaction of sulphide and the remaining oxygen in the medium. The highest rate of reduction (both chemical and biological) was found for Acid Orange 52, the slowest one for acid Orange 6.

ACKNOWLEDGEMENTS

The financial support of Russian Foundation of Basic Research is gratefully acknowledged.

REFERENCES

[1] B. Donlon, E. Razo-Flores, M. Luijten, H.Swarts, G. Lettinga, J. Field: Detoxification and partial mineralization of the azo dye mordant orange 1 in a continuous upflow anaerobic sludge-blanket reactor. *Appl. Microbiol. Biotechnol.,* 47, 83(1997).

[2] S. Kalyuzhnyi, V. Sklyar: Biomineralization of azo dyes and their breakdown products in anaerobic-aerobic hybrid reactors. *Wat. Sci Technol.,* 41(12), 23(2000).

[3] S. Kalyuzhnyi, V. Sklyar, T. Mosolova, I. Kucherenko, J. Russkova, N. Degtyaryova: Methanogenic biodegradation of aromatic amines. *Water Science and Technology,* 42(5-6), 363(2000).

[4] B. Manu, S. Chaudhari: Anaerobic decolorization of simulated textile wastewater containing azo dyes. *Bioresource Technology*, 82, 225(2002).

[5] G. Mcmullan, C. Meehan, A. Conneely, N. Kirby, T. Robinson, P. Nigam, I. M. Banat, R. Marchant, W. F. Smyth: Microbial decolourisation and degradation of textile dyes. *Appl. Microbiol. Biotechnol.,* 56, 81(2001).

[6] E. Razo-Flores: *Biotransformation and Biodegradation of N-substituted Aromatics in Methanogenic Granular Sludge* (Doctoral Thesis). Wageningen University, Wageningen, The Netherlands, 1997. 162 p.

[7] T. Robinson, G. Mcmullan, R. Marchant, P. Nigam: Remediation of dyes in textile effluent: a critical review on current treatment technologies with a proposed alternative. *Bioresource Technology*, 77, 247(2001).

[8] Y. M. Stokar, A. Marechal: Methods of Decoloration of Textile Wastewaters. *Dyes and Pigments,* 37 (4), 335(1998).

[9] N. C. G. Tan: *Integrated and sequential anaerobic/aerobic biodegradation of azo dyes* (Doctoral Thesis). Wageningen University, Wageningen, The Netherlands, 2001. 104 p.

[10] F. Van Der Zee: *Anaerobic azo dye reduction* (Doctoral Thesis). Wageningen University, Wageningen, The Netherlands, 2002.142 p.

In: Biocatalytic Technology and Nanotechnology
Editor: G. E. Zaikov, pp. 51-58
ISBN 1-59454-117-5

Chapter 4

SCREENING OF RHODOCOCCUS SPECIES REVEALING DESULFURIZATION ACTIVITY WITH REGARD TO DIBENZOTHIOPHENE

A. A. Zakharyants, V. P. Murygina and S. V. Kalyuzhnyi
Chemical Enzymology Dept., Chemistry Faculty, Lomonosov Moscow State University,
Vorobiovy Gory 1-11, Moscow, 119899, Russia, Tel. +7(095)939-5083, Факс:+7 (095)
939-5417; e-mail: arpesha@inbox.ru

ABSTRACT

The screening of *Rhodococcus sp.*, capable of utilizing dibenzothiophene (DBT) as a sole sulfur source, was performed. After multiple consecutive passages on the selective medium, *Rhodococcus erythropolis* Ac-1514D and *Rhodococcus ruber* Ac-1513D were adapted to DBT. As a result, the lag periods of these cultures decreased 120 to 20-22 hours. The kinetic parameters, such as the specific growth rates and specific activities of DBT desulfurization by both strains, were calculated. DBT at 0.43mM conversion by *R. erythropolis* was 78-80% to form typical products for 4S-pathway. For the first time, *R. ruber* was also shown to convert DBT (63-65%).

Key words: biodesulfurization, dibenzothiophene, *Rhodococcus sp.*, specific growth rate, specific activity.

INTRODUCTION

To date, more than 200 sulfur-containing organic compounds are identified in crude oil. In general, they are presented as sulfides, mercaptanes and thiophenes. The crude oil from different reservoirs contains 0.03 to 8 % (wt.) sulfur compounds [1]. The content of derivatives of thiophenes in oil depends on their maturity degrees. The high-molecular alkylated derivatives of benzo- and dibenzothiophene in mature oils [2] are most persistent for physical-chemical industrial methods of desulfurization (e.g., hydrodesulfurization). During combustion of sulfur compounds, various gaseous sulfur oxides, such as SO_2 and SO_3 (general name is SO_x), are formed, if not treated they end up as acid rains in atmosphere [3]. This and other facts place stringent requirements for oil fuel quality. Various technologies of oil desulfurization including biological methods are worldwide developed. A number of microorganisms including *Rhodococcus sp.*, able to desulfurize DBT and its derivatives, are described [4, 5, 6, 7, 8, 9, 10, 11]. This process proceeds via so-called 4S-pathway to form sulfite/sulfate and 2-hydroxybiphenyl (2-HBP) derivatives as final products [12, 13, 14, 15, 16, 17] (Fig. 1):

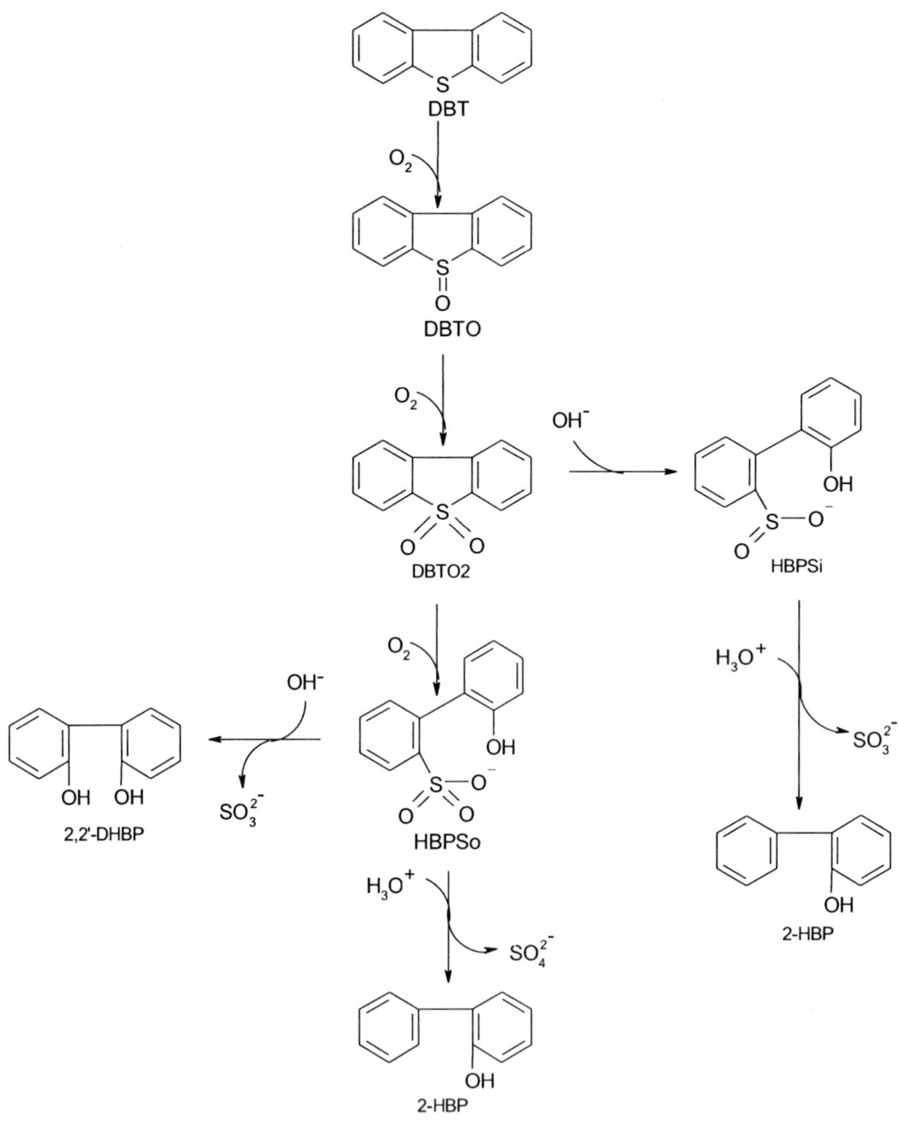

Fig. 1. Scheme of the suggested DBT-metabolizing pathway by *Rhodococcus sp.* DBTO - dibenzothiophene sulfoxide; DBTO2 - dibenzothiophene sulfone; HBPSi - 2-(2'-hydroxy-phenyl)benzene sulfinate; HBPSo - 2-(2'-hydroxyphenyl)benzene sulfonate; 2-HBP - 2-hydroxybiphenyl; 2,2'-DHBP - 2,2'-dihydroxybiphenyl [12, 16].

This paper is concerned with the screening of *Rhodococcus sp.* from our laboratory collection, which can desulfurize DBT, and with the investigation of kinetics of these processes.

MATERIALS AND METHODS

Chemicals

DBT (Sigma-Aldrich, USA) was used as a sole sulfur source for growth of microorganisms on diesel fuel "Z" grade (Russian State Standard No. 305-62) or sodium succinate as carbon source. 2-HBP was obtained from Acros (Germany) and used as standard compound in the Gibbs assay with 2,6-dichloroquinone-4-chloroimide (Acros, Germany) to determine its concentration in culture medium [16]. Other chemicals used were reagent grade and were supplied by "Reahim" and "Laverna" (Russia).

Microorganisms and their Cultivation

Rhodococcus erythropolis Ac-1514D, *Rhodococcus ruber* Ac-1513D and *Rhodococcus rhodochrous* were cultivated in modified Raymond's medium (RM) supplemented with succinate (1% w/v) or diesel oil (0.5% v/v) as carbon source. The medium has the following composition (g/l): Na_2CO_3 – 0,1, $CaCl_2*6H_2O$ - 0,01, $MnCl_2*4H_2O$ - 0,007, $Na_2HPO_4*12H_2O$ - 35,8, KH_2 PO_4 - 13,6, $MgCl_2*6H_2O$ - 0,16, NH_4Cl - 2,0, NaCl - 5,0; the final pH was 6,7. DBT was added in acetone solution after autoclaving (1 atm, 30 min) as a sole sulfur source, the final concentrations in vials were 0.86 mM and 0.43 mM. The strains were also cultured on RM agar plates (20 g/l) containing 200 μM DBT and succinate 1% w/v. The inoculated vials (total volume of 120 ml) containing 40 ml of RM medium were incubated in an orbital shaker (180 rpm, 27 °C) to the end of exponential phase (approximately 90 hours).

Bradford Assay for Intracellular Protein

The growth of microorganisms was monitored by determination of intracellular protein concentration. An aliquot (1 ml) of culture broth was taken ~ every 4 hours. The samples were centrifuged for 15 min at 12000 rpm to separate cells from the supernatant. The cells were disrupted in 1 ml NaOH (3 M) by boiling in water bath for 45 min. Then the samples were centrifuged (12000 rpm, 10 min.) again to separate debris. Bradford reagent (3 ml) (100 mg Coomassie brilliant blue G-250/50 ml in 95% ethanol/100 ml concentrated phosphoric acid and distilled water was added to get 1 l solution) were added to 100 μl of the prepared samples. The optical density at 595 nm was measured after 10 min of colour development.

Phased-Reversed HPLC Assay for DBT

To determine DBT concentrations, 0.5 ml methanol was added to 0.5 ml aliquots of culture broth or else previously, the equal volume (40 ml) of ethyl acetate was added to culture broth and left to stir for 4 h to extract DBT [16]. The prepared probes were analyzed using a Gilson model 302 liquid chromatograph equipped with Du Pont Instruments UV detector (λ=240 nm) and fitted with a phased-reversed Diasorb 130-C_{16}T, 6 μm and loop 20 μm. The column was eluted with vacuum-degassed methanol/water (85:15, v/v); the rate of eluting was 1 ml/min, the pressure was 130 barrel. Approximate retention time of DBT was 7.9 min.

Standard Gibbs Assay for 2-HBP

The reaction with Gibbs reagent was used to determine the concentration of biodesulfurization product - 2-HBP [16]. An aliquots (5 ml) of culture broth supernatant were put into Eppendorf tubes and centrifuged (1200 rpm, 10 min) to remove cells. Supernatant (2 ml) of was transferred to Eppendorf tube, and 20 μl 10 mM (1,985 g/l) Gibbs reagent solution in acetone was added. The assays were incubated over night at 30 °C to complete the colour development. The optical density at 610 nm was measured on a Shimadzu UV-1202 spectrophotometer.

Titration Assay for Sulphite

The filtrated culture broth was titrated with standard iodine solution to determine sulphite [18] according to the following reaction:

$$SO_3^{2-} + H_2O + I_2 \longrightarrow SO_4^{2-} + 2H^+ + 2I^-$$

An aliquot (20 ml) of culture broth was filtered to remove cells and then transferred to a 100 ml Erlenmeyer flask. Five drops of 5% starch solution and concentrated hydrochloric acid to adjust pH to ~2 were added. The assays were titrated with 0.001 N standard iodine solution to get a violet tint.

Turbidometric Assay for Sulphate

The sulfate concentration was determined turbidometrically [18]. An aliquot (20 ml) was filtered through membrane filter (pore diameter 0.4 μm) to remove all cells. The filtrate was transferred to a volumetric flask (100 ml) contaning 20 ml electrolyte solution (60 g NaCl, 5.125 ml HCl/250 ml of the solution) and 15 ml $BaCl_2$ solution (30 g $BaCl_2*2H_2O$/250 ml distilled water). Then, distilled water was added to 100 ml; in 5 min, the optical density was measured at 405 nm.

RESULTS AND DISCUSSION

Three collection cultures of *Rodococcus sp.* were checked for their ability to grow with DBT as a sole sulfur source. It is known [12, 19, 20] that *R. erythropolis* and *R. rhodochrous* are most active in DBT desulfurization. However, in our studies, the desulfurization activity of *R. rhodochrous* for DBT was not undoubtedly established. The duration of lag phase for *R. erythropolis* and *R. ruber* was around 120-122 hours, and the desulfurization activity for DBT was low. Therefore, the two cultures in the selective liquid medium containing DBT 0.43 mM was enriched.

As a result, the enriched cultures of *R. erythropolis* Ac-1514D and *R. ruber* Ac-1513D were obtained by means of three serial subinoculations in the above liquid medium. The lag phases were reduced to 20-22 hours for both cultures (Fig. 2 and Fig. 3).

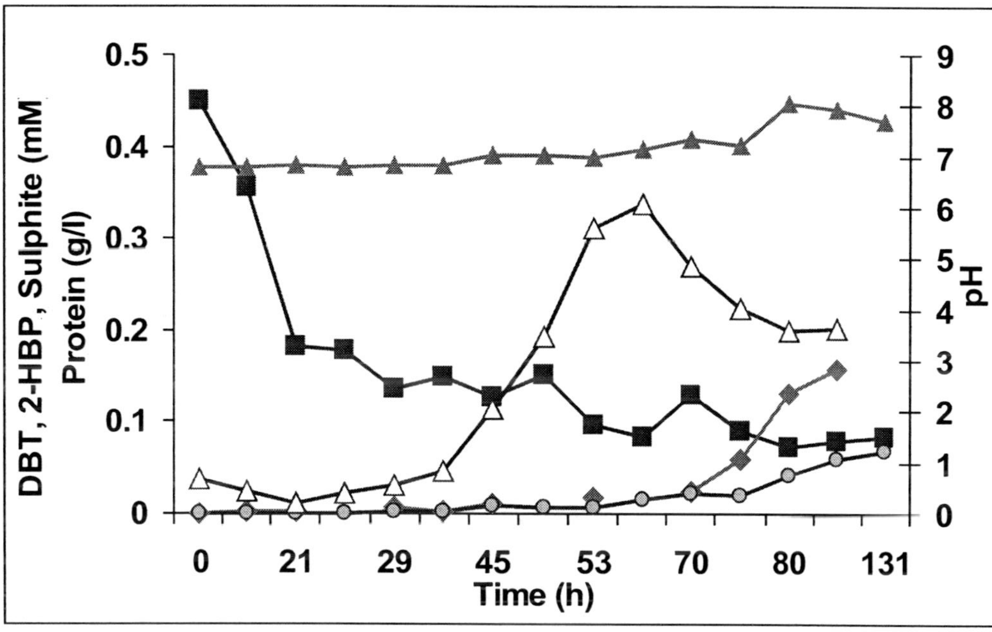

Fig. 2. Time course of DBT desulfurization by *R. erythropolis* Ac-1514D. Ac-1514D was cultivated at 27 °C in RM with 0.43 mM DBT as a sole sulfur source. ■, DBT (mM); Δ, protein (g/l); ◆, 2-HBP (mM); ●, sulphite (mM); ▲ pH.

The typical curves of DBT conversion, biomass growth and accumulation of biodesulfurization products are presented (Fig. 2 and Fig. 3). DBT biodesulfurization data were processed using the Monod equation as described [64]. The specific growth rates (μ) of two enriched strains were obtained by the analysis of the linear ranges of the growth curves (cell protein vs time) in the semi-logarithmic coordinates. The μ values of *R. erythropolis* Ac-1514D and *R. ruber* Ac-1513D were actually identical: $0{,}080 \pm 0{,}006\ h^{-1}$ и $0{,}086 \pm 0{,}004\ h^{-1}$, respectively. The obtained values for *Rodococcus sp.* are 2.5 times less than known so far in literature for *R. erythropolis* [9, 21]. The yield coefficients for our cultures were $0{,}86 \pm 0{,}04$ and $5{,}85 \pm 0{,}3$ g protein/mmol DBT for *R. erythropolis* and *R. ruber*, respectively. Using these data, the specific activities were determined for both cultures: 185 mmol DBT (kg dry wt)$^{-1}$h^{-1} and 30 mmol DBT (kg dry wt)$^{-1}$h^{-1} for *R. erythropolis* and *R. ruber*, respectively.

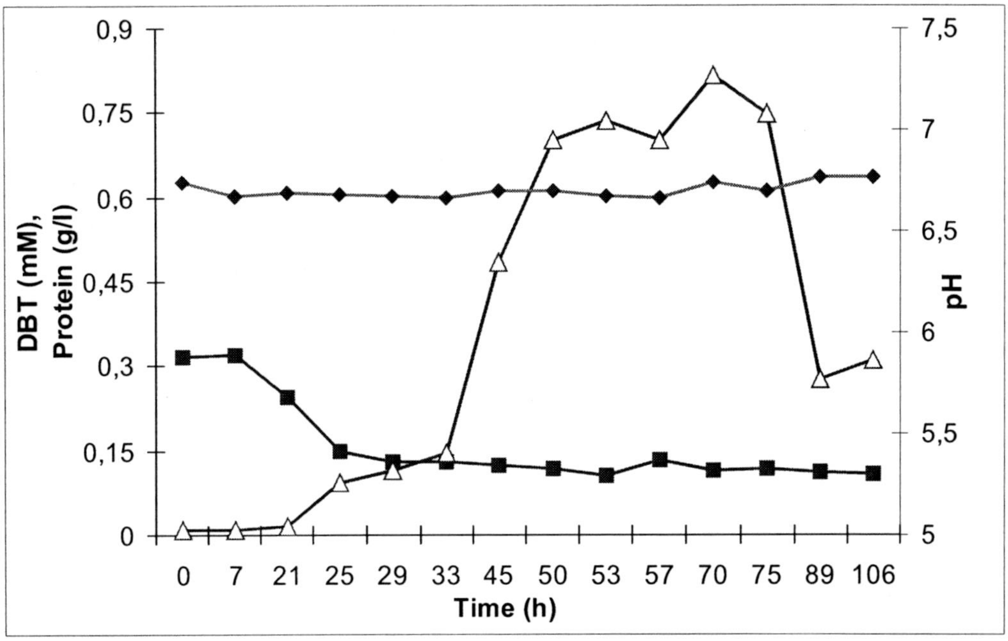

Fig. 3. Time course of DBT conversion by *R. ruber* Ac-1513D. Ac-1513D was cultivated at 27 °C in RM with 0.43 mM DBT as a sole sulfur source. ■, DBT (mM); Δ, protein (g/l); ◆, 2-HBP (mM); ●, sulphite (mM); ▲ pH.

The specific activity of *R. erythropolis* Ac-1514D characterizing its ability to desulfurize DBT to 2-HBP was 80 mmol 2-HBP (kg dry wt)$^{-1}$h^{-1}. The obtained data are in accordance with those determined for non-mutant *Rhodococcus sp.* [4, 9, 20].

Since *R. ruber* Ac-1513D was never characterized as desulfurizing microorganism, this paper represents the first report indicating DBT desulfurization by this bacterium. The DBT conversions, about 63-65 %, were observed after 80 hours of growth with the initial concentration of DBT 0.43 mM (Fig. 3).

Earlier, it was established that biodesulfurization of DBT by *Rhodococcus sp.* proceeded via so-called 4S-pathway [12, 13, 16, 17, 22]. The dead products were sulfite and 2-HBP. Other biodesulfurization paths were not proposed. The analysis of data obtained for *R. erythropolis* (Fig. 2) and *R. ruber* (Fig. 3) suggest that 4S-pathway occurred in our case.

CONCLUSIONS

Thus, the desulfurizing ability and activity of *R. erythropolis* and *R. ruber* were established and investigated.

The consecutive passages on the selective medium of both strains allowed us to obtain active cultures with regard to DBT desulfurization. A six-fold decrease of the lag phase durations was reached. However, we did not succeed in our attempts to adapt to DBT *R. rhodochrous*, which is known as the bacteria showing the desulfurizing activity.

The conversion of DBT (initial concentration 0.43 mM) according to 4S-pathway by *R. erythropolis* and *R. ruber* was investigated. Thus, some kinetic parameters, such as specific growth rates and specific activities of DBT desulfurization, were determined.

REFERENCES

[1] M. J. Grossman, M. K. Lee, R. C. Prince, K. K. Garrett, G. N. George, I. J. Pickerin: Microbial Desulfurization of a Crude Oil Middle-Distillate Fraction: Analysis of the Extent of Sulfur Removal and the Effect of Removal on Remaining Sulfur. *App. Environ. Microbiol.*, 65 (1), 181 (1999).

[2] C. Marcelis: *Anaerobic Biodesulfurization of Thiophenes.* The Netherlands. Thesis Wageningen University, 2002, 178 p.

[3] D.J. Monticello, W.R. Finnerty: Microbial Desulfurization of Fossil Fuels. *Annu. Rev. Microbiol.*, 39, 371 (1985).

[4] M. Kobayashi, T. Onaka, Y. Ishii, J. Konishi, M. Takaki, H. Okada, Y. Ohta, K. Koizumi, M. Suzuki: Desulfurization of Alkylated Forms of Both Dibenzothiophene and Benzothiophene by a Single Bacterial Strain. *FEMS Microbiol. Lett.*, 187, 123 (2000).

[5] J. Hirasawa, Y. Ishii, M. Kobayashi, K. Koizumi, K. Maruhashi: Improvement of Desulfurization Activity in *Rhodococcus erythropolis* KA2-5-1 by Genetic Engineering. Biosci. Biotech. Biochem., 65, 239 (2001).

[6] H. Okada, N. Numura, T. Nakahara, K. Muruhashi: Cultivation of Desulfurizing Bacterium, *Mycobacterium* sp. G3. *Biotechnol. Lett.*, 23, 2047 (2001).

[7] H. Okada, N. Numura, T. Nakahara, K. Muruhashi: Analysis of Substrate Specificity of the Desulfurizing Bacterium *Mycobacterium* sp. G3. *J. Biosc. Bioeng.*, 93, 228 (2002).

[8] B.R. Folsom, D.R. Schieche, P.M. Digrazia, J. Werner, S. Palmer: Microbial Desulfurization of Alkylated Dibenzothiophenes from a Hydrodesulfurized Middle Distillate by *Rhodococcus erythropolis* I19. *App. Environ. Microbiol.*, 65 (11), 4967 (1999).

[9] E.N. Kaufman, J.B. Hankins, A.P. Borole: Comparison of Batch-stirred and Electro-spray Reactors for Biosulfurization of Dibenzothiophene in Crude Oil and Hydrocarbon Feedstocks. *App. Biochem. Biotechnol.*, 73, 127 (1998).

[10] P. Wang, S. Krawiec: Kinetic Analysis of Desulfurization of Dibenzothiophene by *Rhodococcus erythropolis* in Continuous Cultures. *App. Environ. Microbiol.*, 62 (5), 1670 (1996a).

[11] P. Wang, A.E. Humphey, S. Krawiec: Kinetic Analysis of Desulfurization of Dibenzothiophene by *Rhodococcus erythropolis* in Continuous Cultures. *App. Environ. Microbiol.*, 62 (8), 3066 (1996b).

[12] L. Setti, P. Farinelli, S. Di Martino, S. Frassinetti, G. Lanzarini, P.G. Pifferi: Developments in Destructive and Non-destructive Pathways for Selective Desulfurizations in Oil-biorefining processes. *App Microbiol. Biotechnol.*, 52, 111 (1999).

[13] P. Wang, S. Krawiec: Desulfurization of Dibenzothiophene to 2-hydroxybiphenyl by Some Newly Isolated Bacterial Strains. *Arch. Microbiol.*, 161, 266 (1994).

[14] K. Kodama, K. Umehara, S. Nakatanni, Y. Minoda, K. Yamada: Identification of Microbial Products from Dibenzothiophene and its Proposed Oxidation Pathway. *Agr. Biol. Chem.*, 37, 45 (1973).

[15] J.R. Gallagher, E.S. Olson, D.C. Stanly: Microbial Desulfurization of Dibenzothiophene: a Sulfur Specific Pathway. *FEMS Microbiol. Lett.*, 107, 31 (1993).

[16] C. Oldfield, O. Pogrebinsky, J. Simmonds, E.S. Olson, C.F. Kulpa: Elucidation of Metabolic pathway for Dibenzothiophene Desulfurization by *Rhodococcus* sp. stain IGTS8 (ATCC 53968). *Microbiology,* 143, 2961 (1997).

[17] K.A. Gray, O.S. Pogrebinsky, T. Mrachko, L. Xi, D.J. Montecello, C.H. Squires: Molecular Mechanisms of Biocatalytic Desulfurization of Fossil Fuels. *Nat. Biotechnol.,* 14, 1705 (1996).

[18] U.U. Lurye: *Analytical Chemistry of Industrial Wastewater*. Khimiya, Moscow, 1984, 447 p. (in Russian).

[19] K.J. Kayser, B.A. Bielaga-Jones, K. Jackowski, O. Odusan, J.J. Kilbane: Utilization of Organosulfur Compounds by Axenic and Mixed Cultures of *Rhodococcus rhodochrous* IGTS8. *J.Gen. Microbiol.,* 139, 3123 (1993).

[20] H. Honda, H. Sugiyama, I. Saito, T. Kobayashi: High Cell Density Culture of *Rhodococcus rhodochrous* by pH-stat Feeding and Dibenzothiophene Degradation. *J. Ferment Bioeng.,* 85, 334 (1998).

[21] J.H. Chang, Y.K. Chang, K.-S. Cho, H.N. Chang: Desulfurization of Model and Diesel Oils by Resting Cells of *Gordona* sp. *Biotechnol. Lett.,* 22, 193 (2000).

[22] D.C. Bressler, J.A. Norman, P.M. Fedorak: Ring Cleavage of Sulfur Heterocycles: How Does it Happen? *Biodegradation.*, 8, 297 (1998).

In: Biocatalytic Technology and Nanotechnology
Editor: G. E. Zaikov, pp. 59-63
ISBN 1-59454-117-5

Chapter 5

MAGNETIC CARRIERS BIOLOGICAL PREPARATIONS FOR DIAGNOSTICS AND THERAPY OF ONCOLOGICAL DISEASES

***N. A. Brusentsov*[1], *T. N. Brusentsova*[2], *A. Yu. Baryshnikov*[1], *A. M. Yunin*[3], *F. S. Bayburtskiy*[3], *V. D. Kuznetsov*[2] *and L. Kh. Komissarova*[3]**

[1] N. N. Blokhin Russian Oncological Research Center RAMS, Moscow, 115478, Kashyrskoye Shosse, 24, telephone:111 – 83 – 41, E - mail: *pol@dialup.ptt.ru*

[2] D. I. Mendeleev University of Chemical Technology of Russia, Moscow, 125047, Miusskaya Place, 9, telephone: 112 – 28 – 10, E - mail:*gala752@mail.ru*

[3] N. M. Emanuel Institute of Biochemical Physics RAS, Moscow, 119991, Kosygina Street, 4, telephone: 936 – 17 – 45, E - mail: *Bayburt@mail.ru*

ABSTRACT

In the present article the review of studies devoted to the preparation and use of immunomagnetic materials used in medical and biological investigations was made. The opportunity for creation of non-toxic and biodegradable magnetic carriers used in diagnostics was shown on the basis of magnetic microspheres.

Key words: Magnetic microspheres, dextranferrite, magnetic sorbents, immunomagnetic materials, monoclonal antibody.

For last decades a method of immunomagnetic separation of sub-cellular structures and cells based on use of monoclonal antibodies, fixed on a surface of magnetic carriers microspheres has quickly started to develop. For definition of ways for the preparation of magnetic carriers materials used in diagnostics, in transplantation of marrow and blood marrow cells, the authors carried out the review of the scientific publications.

The surface of microspheres formed from polystyrole, polyglutaric aldehyde, polyacrolein, provided an opportunity for adsorption and chemical sorption of monoclonal antibodies. Formed conjugates specifically contacted with objects - targets, and moved directionally in a magnetic field, carrying away targets behind themselves in conformity with increase of constant magnetic field gradient. This method was used for the isolation of proteins, nucleic acids, chromosomes, cells and microorganisms from biological liquids. The methods of preparation of magnetic microspheres and immunomagnetic sorbents were developed by Dynal company (Oslo, Norway). The immunomagnetic sorbents Dynabeads M-270, coated with specific antibodies to tumour cells of blood and marrow, were successfully used for diagnostics and treatment of oncological diseases. The sensitivity of the method enabled one to detect 1 tumour cell in 1 ml of blood. Magnetic microspheres prepared on the basis of polyvinyl alcohol, were applied for the separation of nucleic acids.

For the separation of cells high gradient magnetic fields were used. The various types of magnetic materials for manufacturing of constant magnets used in devices for magnetic separation of cells were considered. The methods of their tests and physical characteristics were given. As an example of successful use of magnetic systems for the isolation of blood marrow cells, quadrupolic magnetic high-efficiency (10^7 cells / sec) flowing separator can serve.

Sticking of immunomagnetic particles specific to antigen and cytokine receptors on tumour cells was determined by magnetophoresis. Not less than 200 of tumour necrosis factor receptor molecules were determined on a tumour cell with the help of streptavidin-coated particles, which conjugated with previously biotinilated tumour necrosis factor molecules used as ligands.

Depending on a toxicity level magnetic microspheres and magnetic sorbents were applied as follows:

1. Dextranferrite and conjugates of dextranferrite with ligands, magnetite-dextran and conjugates of magnetite-dextran with antibodies were left on cells; the magnetic microspheres had low toxicity and were completely metabolized in organism of mammals.
2. Detached from cells by enzymes or releasing peptide; the magnetic microspheres (polystyrene magnetic sorbents) were not metabolized in organism, they have high toxicity.

All magnetic sorbents prepared on the basis of synthetic polymeric magnetic microspheres (diameter 0,1 – 6 microns) with ferro- or ferrimagnetics incapsulated in them, were toxic, as they were not metabolized in organism of the patient and caused thrombosis. Therefore, after allocation of a complex «the cells - magnetic sorbents» it was necessary to pinch off magnetic sorbent from cells by enzymatic action, but as a result of this manipulation the surfaces of cell membranes could change. Considerably more selective and softer releasing peptides act, but during replacement of cells from complexes «the cells - magnetic sorbent» by releasing peptides, for each new complex it was necessary to use specific releasing peptides.

The listed scientific publications were devoted to creation of non-toxic magnetic carriers microspheres, non-toxic immunomagnetic sorbents, development and application of methods of immunomagnetic separation of antigenes used for transplantation of blood marrow cells.

There was no necessity to pinch off non-toxic immunomagnetic sorbent in a complex «non-toxic magnetic sorbent – cells», as it, as a rule, did not interfere with its functional properties. This discovery has allowed to replace toxic magnetic sorbents, which are to be necessarily pinched off from cells, by non-toxic magnetic sorbents not requiring to be pinched off.

Taking into account the importance of non-toxic magnetic sorbents in separation of blood marrow cells, we have presented one of ways of their synthesis and methods of initial substances preparation which are necessary for it. The non-toxic magnetic sorbents were prepared on a basis of magnetite, dextran and specific antibodies:

1. A surface of magnetite crystals, activated with Cl^- ions, is coated by dextran, and magnetic microspheres of dextranferrite are prepared;
2. The magnetic microspheres of dextranferrite processed under the common scheme: a surface of magnetic microspheres of dextranferrite oxidized by the action of potassium periodate (KIO_4) or sodium periodate ($NaIO_4$); thus, magnetic microspheres of polyaldehyddextranferrite were prepared; they were incubated with monoclonal antibodies and conjugates were obtained, representing non-toxic immunomagnetic sorbents.

The chemical scheme of synthesis of non-toxic magnetic sorbents on a basis of dextranferrite and monoclonal antibodies:

$$(\gamma\text{-}Fe_2O_3)_{r\text{-}m}(Fe_2O_3FeO)_m(C_6H_9O_5)_f(C_6H_{10}O_5)_{q\text{-}f} \xrightarrow{+KIO_4}$$

$$(\gamma\text{-}Fe_2O_3)_{r\text{-}m}(Fe_2O_3FeO)_m(C_6H_9O_5)_f(C_6H_{10}O_5)_{q\text{-}f\text{-}j}(C_4H_4O_4)_j \xrightarrow{+H_2N\text{-}R}$$

$$(\gamma\text{-}Fe_2O_3)_{r\text{-}m}(Fe_2O_3FeO)_m(C_6H_9O_5)_f(C_6H_{10}O_5)_{q\text{-}f\text{-}j}(C_4H_6O_4N\text{-}R)_j$$

r – number of molecules in a crystal nucleus of ferrite;
m – number of residues of iron oxide molecules, connected to ions of chlorine or glucose residues;
q – number of glucose residues in dextran molecules;
f – number of glucose residues, connected with iron oxide;
j – number of glucose residues, connected with immunoglobulin;
R – immunoglobulin.

Oxidation of dextranferrite by sodium periodate was carried out at + 20°C for 30 minutes. The immunomagnetic sorbent, which was prepared on the basis of polyaldehydedextranferrite magnetic microspheres and monoclonal antibodies, comprised itself a conjugate having a diameter of a crystal nucleus 10 nm, diameter of mycelle 300 nm, number of particles up to $1.5 \cdot 10^9$ / g, specific magnetization saturation 3 – 12 $A \cdot m^2$/ kg; at doses applied it was non-toxic, as it completely metabolized in organism of mammals. After allocation in a non-uniform constant magnetic field of a complex «polyaldehyddextranferrite – monoclonal antibody – cells» it was not necessary to pinch off conjugate «polyaldehyddextranferrite – monoclonalic antibody» from a cells, as it was non-toxic at doses used. The electrokinetic potential of dextranferrite equalled + 15 mV at pH 6,6; LD_{50} of dextranferrite was 5 g/kg at intravenous injection in mice. At intravenous and intraperitoneum injection in mice in natural conditions, dextranferrite collected in liver and in spleen. At intraarterial regional injection in dogs in a non-uniform constant magnetic field, dextranferrite concentrated in places with the maximal gradient of a constant magnetic field and inductionally heated from + 43 to 46 °C in a variable magnetic field at frequencies from 50 to 1000 kHz.

The magnetic microspheres and monoclonal antibodies were necessary for preparation of immunomagnetic sorbents. Developed in the 70s, the hybridomic technology was used as the basic way of preparation of monoclonal antibodies. The process of preparation of pure lines of «antibody – producing cells» besides gene-engineering manipulations included: separation of cells, screening and cloning of formed hybridomas. The listed procedures were labour-consuming. One of possible variants of modernization allowing to considerably reduce time and to raise quantity of hybridomic cells, consisted of the use of immunomagnetic separation of desired clones. The supernatants of all colonies formed were tested by a method of solid-phase immunoenzymatic analysis (ELISA) for revealing of producers of anti-hCG-antibody. Chemically connecting received hCG-antigene with magnetic microspheres Dynabeads M450 (Dynal, Norway) of immunomagnetic sorbents - anti-hCG-M450 were prepared and with the help of immunomagnetic separation positive colonies were allocated. The antigen-specific hybridomas were separated from non-secreting cells with the use of SmCo magnet. The cells of a positive fraction connected to particles of sorbent, were repeatedly dissolved in medium and dispersed on 96-well plates. The stage of preparation of cultures of producer cells was done directly following immunomagnetic separation, omitting a stage of pinching off the sorbent, which usually represented difficulty in positive immunomagnetic separation. The hybridomas, isolated by this way, secreted high affinity (more than $1 \cdot 10^{9}$ моle $^{-1}$) monoclonal antibody of one isotype.

Conclusion

Now biomagnetic sorbents are successfully applied for immunomagnetic separation of cells. The works on creation of magnetic microcarriers on a basis of silicaorganic polysterene and dextranferrite matrices are carried out. The methods of synthesis of microspheres of various dispersity were developed, the different ways of surface particles activation allowing to conjugate them with monoclonal antibodies were tested. The application of cell sorting for reconstruction transplantology following courses of massive chemi- and beam therapy allows to considerably lower haematotoxic complication of conservative treatment of oncological patients and to reduce terms of their rehabilitation. The combination of positive and negative sorting allows to receive homogeneous preparations of minor subpopulations of cells for biotherapy (dendrite cells for creation of vaccines). An urgent task of positive sorting remains a problem of maintenance of controlled destruction of a complex «microparticle – cells», as after the extraction the cells intended for autotransplantation should remain functionally active for reproduction and not to contain on their surface biologically active or inert particles. The way out in the given situation can be the use of biodegradable dextranferrite nanoparticles as a matrix of immunosorbent. Also possible is an application of molecules as binding ligands between active ligands and matrix, which do not injure vital ability of cells.

ACKNOWLEDGEMENTS

The work was carried out at financing the grants RFBR № 02 - 01 - 00694 and Moscow governments № 113 / 03 – ГП – M.

REFERENCES

[1] Brusentsov N. A., Burova O. S., Baryshnikov A. Yu., Brusentsova T. N., Moshechkov N. G., Makhlin R. C.: *Application of biomagnetic carriers in medicine. Book of abstracts.* Moscow, N. M. Emanuel Institute of biochemical physics RAS, P. 60 – 67, 2002 (в России).

[2] Fillippov V. I., Ivanov P. K., Blokhin D. Yu., Kurbatova E. S., Ershov O. L., Zhigalin G. Ya., Bogoslovskaya E. V., Shypulin G. A.: *X International conference on magnetic fluids. Book of abstracts.* Ivanovo - Plyos, P. 305 - 307, 2002 (in Russian)

[3] Khrustalyova I. P., Moskovtsev A. A., Ivanov P. K., Blokhin D. Yu., Ershov O. L., Fillippov V. I., Zhigalin G. Ya., Moshechkov N. G., Machlin R. S.: *X International conference on magnetic fluids. Book of abstracts.* Ivanovo - Plyos, P. 313 - 317, 2002 (in Russian)

[4] Golenkina E. A., Moskovtsev A. A., Ivanov P. K., Blokhin D. Yu., Ershov O. L., Fillippov V. I., Baryshnikov A. Yu., Moshechkov N. G., Makhlin R. C.: *X International conference on magnetic fluids. Book of abstracts.* Ivanovo - Plyos, P. 343 - 346, 2002 (in Russian).

In: Biocatalytic Technology and Nanotechnology
Editor: G. E. Zaikov, pp. 65-71
ISBN 1-59454-117-5

Chapter 6

EXPRESSION OF RECOMBINANT ORGANOPHOSPHORUS HYDROLASE IN ACTIVE FORM

E. N. Efremenko, Yu. A. Votchitseva, T. K. Aliev and S. D. Varfolomeyev
Chemical Enzymology Department, The M.V.Lomonosov Moscow State University, Vorobiovy Gory, 1/11, Moscow, 119992, Russia, e-mail: efremenko@enzyme.chem.msu.ru

ABSTRACT

The influences of host strain, cultivation temperature, inducer concentration and the duration of induction period on the expression of recombinant organophosphosphate hydrolase (OPH) in *E.coli* cells were investigated. To enhance the yield of biosynthesis of OPH in soluble and active catalytic form, the co-expression of OPH with several types of chaperones was investigated. It was revealed that following conditions of cell growth are optimal for protein expression in *E.coli* DH5α cells transformed with pTES-OPH plasmid: 0.2-0.3 mM isopropyl β-D-galactopyranoside, 30^{0}C, 20-22 hours of induction of protein synthesis. This regime guaranteed isolation of 12 mg of highly pure and catalytically active protein from 1 g of wet cell biomass.

Key words: organophosphate hydrolase, protein expression, chaperones

INTRODUCTION

Organoposphate hydrolase (aryldiacylphosphatase, EC 3.1.8.1) is a highly effective catalyst for hydrolysis of various organophosphorus (OP) compounds, including pesticides (coumaphos, malathion, diazinon, etc.) widely used in agriculture and chemical warfare agents (VX, Sarin, Soman) which should be destroyed [1-3]. The presence of OP compounds was revealed in soils, streams, ground and waste water, food, textile products, and even in domestic dust [4]. The real needs for this enzyme for the differential analysis of OP pesticides [5-7] and degradation of OP neurotoxins [8] are obvious. Hence, the main interest of specialists is focused on the enhancement of yield of recombinant OPH in *E.coli* cells [9-12]. It is well known that the level of protein expression depends on both the genetic construction comprising the gene coding for the target protein and host strain biosynthetic potential depending on its genotype and cultivation conditions. The rise of yield of required protein can result in its overproduction leading to non-effective folding and formation of its inactive aggregates known as inclusion bodies. There are multiple approaches to increase the synthesis of an active soluble form of proteins. In the present work, we investigated the influence of the following factors on the expression of OPH in *E.coli* cells: 1) reduction of protein synthesis rate by means of cell cultivation at a lower temperature or by using fewer amounts of transcription inducer; 2) co-expression of a target protein with molecular chaperones [13].

Materials and Methods

Expression of OPH in Escherichia Coli Cells

E.coli strains were cultivated at 30^0C or 37^0C under agitation (180 rpm) in the Luria-Bertani (LB) broth or TYE medium [14] supplemented with 100 μg ml^{-1} ampicillin for expression of *opd* (*o*rganophosphate-*d*egrading)-gene encoding synthesis of OPH alone or with addition of 50 μg ml^{-1} chloramphenicol for co-expression of OPH with chaperones. Plasmid pTES-OPH with cloned *opd*-gene derived from the chromosomal DNA of *Pseudomonas diminuta* was constructed as described previously [15].

Two different plasmids [16] coding for the synthesis of chaperones were used for the transformation of *E.coli* cells and further co-expression of these proteins with OPH. The first one was plasmid pOFXtac-SL2 (pELS) containing operon coding for synthesis of GroEL and GroES chaperones. The other plasmid pOFXtac-KJE2 (pKJE) contained operon coding for synthesis of DnaJ, DnaK chaperones and GrpE.

The *E.coli* strains DH5α and W3110 were used for transformation with plasmid pTES-OPH and *opd*-gene expression. To study the co-expression of chaperones and OPH, the *E.coli* DH5α cells were transformed subsequently with one of the plasmids harbouring chaperones genes and, then, with pTES-OPH plasmid.

Induction was triggered by different concentrations (up to 0.7 mM) of isopropyl β-D-galactopyranoside (IPTG) in the early log phase of cell growth. The Co^{2+} ions (0.1 mM) were added at the same step to enhance the expression of active OPH form. To analyze the protein synthesis, cells were harvested by centrifugation (5,000 g, 30 min), suspended in sonication buffer (50 mM Tris-HCl, pH 8.6 with 100 mM NaCl and 1 mM EDTA) and disrupted by 5-s pulsed sonication (45% efficient time) on ice. The disrupted cell suspension was subsequently centrifuged at 15,000 g (40 min), and the supernatant was used as fraction containing the soluble form of OPH whereas the precipitate was investigated as insoluble fraction. The protein content in both forms was analyzed by 12% SDS-PAGE followed by Coomassie R-250 staining and subsequent densitometry analysis of band intensities. Protein concentration was determined by the modified Lowry method.

Assay of OPH Activity

Purification of OPH was conducted in accordance with previously published procedure [9,17]. Enzymatic activity was routinely measured with 1 mM paraoxon in 50 mM CHES buffer (pH 9.0) using spectrophotometer, at 25^{0}C. The change in absorbance at 405 nm corresponding to the accumulation of p-nitrophenolate ion was recorded. One unit of enzymatic activity was defined as the hydrolysis of 1 μmole of paraoxon per minute. The enzymatic activity of cells was monitored during the cell cultivation and it was determined using the cell biomass directly. The specific activity of cells was calculated in respect to the unit of cell wet weight. The last one was detected by measuring the optical density of cell suspension at 540 nm and using the calibration curves.

RESULTS AND DISCUSSION

Effect of Temperature on the OPH Expression

The influence of temperature conditions on the OPH synthesis and folding appeared to be considerable. According to electrophoresis data (data not shown), the cultivation of both tested strains at 37^{0}C resulted in accumulation of OPH in a high yield. Its total yield amounted to 15% and 50% of total cell protein in the strains *E.coli* DH5α and W3110, respectively. The part of insoluble fraction was 3-4 times higher than that of soluble form for *E.coli* DH5α cells. *E.coli* W3110 cells provided the synthesis of OPH where the most part of the recombinant protein (95%) was in the form of inclusion bodies. Since then, all further experiments were conducted using *E.coli* DH5α strain as host cells for accumulation of soluble OPH form.

The reduction of cultivation temperature down to 30^{0}C allowed the two-fold enhancement of OPH active form yield. This temperature was used in further studies of the expression of recombinant OPH.

Effect of Inducer Concentration on OPH Expression

It was found that OPH expression in the absence of IPTG in the developed system, comprising host cells and constructed plasmid, guaranteed the basal level of OPH synthesis in the amount equal to 1-3 % of total cell protein. The introduction of very low IPTG concentration (0.01 mM) into the nutrient medium was shown to result in three-fold increase of OPH synthesis in active form compared to the level obtained without IPTG. The search for the optimal IPTG concentration inducing the maximal synthesis of soluble OPH in the cells as well as the optimal duration of this process was undertaken. The curves of cell growth and enzymatic activity of cells growing up in presence of different concentrations of IPTG are presented in Figs.1 and 2, respectively. According to the results obtained, the higher concentration of IPTG was used for the induction of OPH synthesis, the lower cell growth rate was observed. Comparison of the amount of cell biomass accumulated during the cultivation with the maximum of specific cell activity defined the 0.2-0.3 mM IPTG as the best concentration for reaching the high level of OPH expression in the developed system.

The duration of cell cultivation providing the highest yield of soluble OPH was 20-22 hours. The longer period of cell cultivation was characterized by further increase in the total protein concentration accumulated in the cells and, as a result, the reduction of part of "correctly folded" active form of OPH was observed and confirmed by enzymatic activity as well as by electrophoresis data (data not shown).

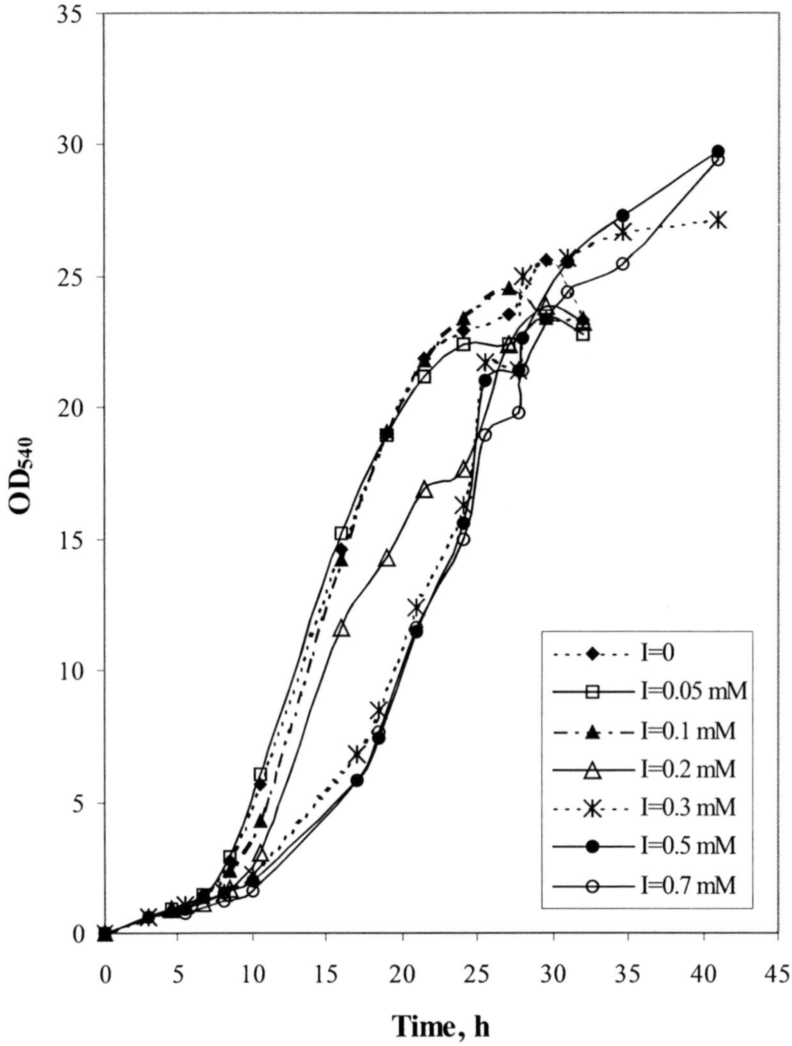

Fig.1. The growth of *E.coli* DH5α pTES-OPH cells in the medium supplied with different concentrations of IPTG (I).

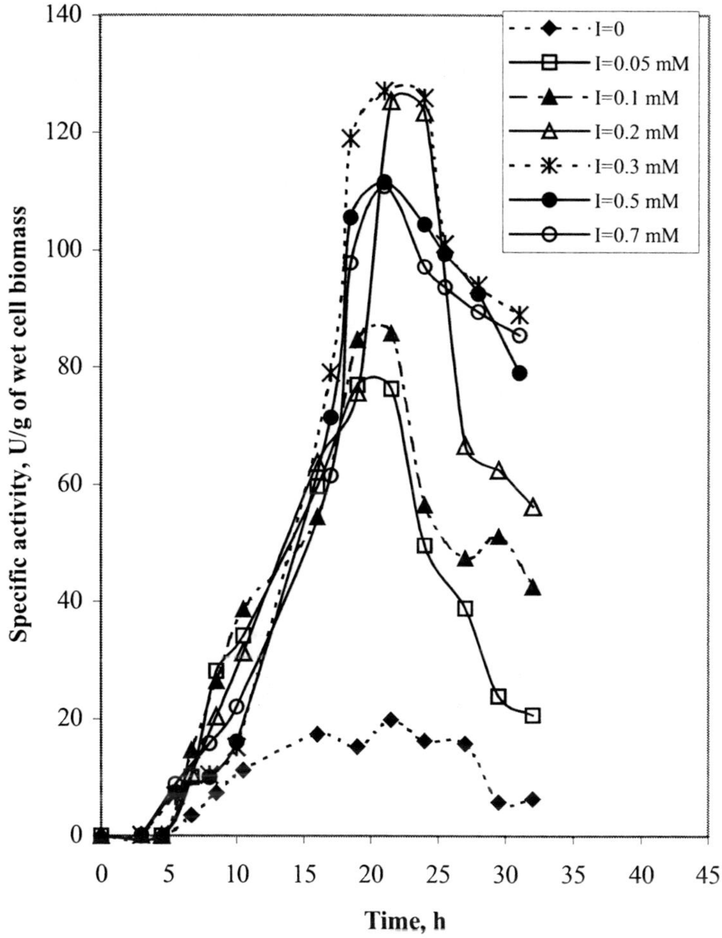

Fig.2. Dependence of enzymatic activity accumulated in *E.coli* DH5α pTES-OPH cells vs. time of cell cultivation and IPTG (I) concentration.

The Influence of Co-Expression with Chaperones on OPH Solubility

According to literature data [13, 16], the co-expression of some protein with molecular chaperones can promote the right folding of synthesized protein, enhancing its yield in active form. Since the correct mechanism of OPH folding is unknown, the investigation of OPH co-expression with chaperones was conducted with application of two different plasmids: pELS and pKJE. The chaperones DnaJ, DnaK and GrpE were shown not to influence the OPH expression, whereas the presence of increased amounts of GroEL and GroES chaperones positively influenced the synthesis of soluble form of OPH providing a two-fold increase in its percentage in the total protein cell content. That was confirmed by the enzymatic activity measurements as well as by electrophoretic analysis. Nevertheless, note that the co-expression of OPH with both groups of chaperones resulted in 50% decrease of the total biosynthesis yield of this enzyme. Furthermore, the period of cell cultivation with the inducer necessary to reach the maximal cell activity was 1.5 times longer when the simultaneous presence of plasmids coding for OPH and chaperones took place. This decrease in cell growth rate might have been caused by presence of two actively expressed genetic constructs within cells.

Purification of Recombinant OPH Obtained Under Optimized Conditions of Protein Expression

The optimization of conditions of protein expression in *E.coli* DH5α cells transformed with pTES-OPH cells provided the high yield of the required enzyme. The regular procedure of OPH isolation and purification allowed the preparation of 12 mg of highly purified enzyme from 1 g of wet cell biomass (Table 1). The average specific activity of OPH was 5,800 U/mg protein in respect to paraoxon.

Table 1. Purification summary of OPH isolation from 1 g of wet cell biomass.

Stage of purification	Total protein, mg	Total activity, U	Specific activity, U/mg of protein	Purification factor, (fold)	Yield, %
Cell sonication	341	101217	297	1	100
Streptomycin sulphate	85.2	86034	1010	4	85
Ammonium sulphate	40	78949	1974	8.5	78
S-Sepharose	19.3	73888	3828	17.7	73
DEAE-column	12	69840	5820	28.4	69

The final results testified to the development of biological system which can be used under optimized conditions for overproduction of catalytically active OPH. This system can be used to scale up the biotechnological production of OPH, thus promoting the application of the enzyme as a component of biosensors for OP detection as well as an active substance of immobilized preparations using different carriers including textile materials for the individual protection of agricultural and military personnel against the real and potential action of OP neurotoxins.

ACKNOWLEDGEMENTS

We are grateful to Dr. Olivier Fayet, Laboratoire de Microbiologie et Genetique Moleculaires, CNRS, Toulouse, France for kindly providing us with plasmids pOFXtac-SL2 and pOFXtac-KJE2.

This work was financially supported by Russian Foundation for Basic Research Grant # 02-04-48981.

REFERENCES

[1] J. K.Grimsley, V. K.Rastogi, J. R.Wild: *Bioremediation: Principles and Practice - Biodegradation Technology Developments*/Ed. S.K. Sikdar, R.L.Irvine,: Technomic Publishing Company Inc., Notre Dame/Indiana, II, 577 (1998).

[2] B. Zwanenburg et al. (Eds.) *Enzymes in Action: Green Solutions for Chemical Problems.* Kluwer Academic Publishers, Dordrecht-Boston-London, 2000. 458 p.

[3] E.N. Efremenko, V.S. Sergeeva: *Russian Chem. Bull., Intern. Edition,* 50 (10), 1826 (2001).

[4] M. Fukushima, Y. Yamaguchi: *Biochemistry*, 23, 74 (1994).

[5] A.L.Simonian, E.N.Efremenko, J.R. Wild: *Anal.Chim. Acta*, 444, 179 (2001).

[6] A. Mulchandani, W. Chen, P. Mulchandani, J. Wang, K.R. Rogers: *Biosens. & Bioelectron.,* 16 (4-5), 225 (2001).

[7] A.W. Flounders, J.V. Volponi, K. Wally, J.S. Schoeniger, S.C. Carichner, A.S. Simonian, A.K. Singh, J.R. Wild: *Biosens. & Bioelectron.*, 14, (8-9), 715 (1999).

[8] S. Varfolomeyev, I. Kurochkin, A.Eremenko, E. Efremenko: *Pure & Appl. Chem.*, 74 (12), 2311 (2002).

[9] J.K.Grimsley, J.M.Scholtz, C.N.Pace, J.R.Wild: *Biochemistry*, 36 (47), 14366 (1997).

[10] C.M. Serdar, D.C. Murdock, M.F. Rohde: *Bio/technology*, 7, 1151 (1989).

[11] C.F. Wu, J.J. Valdes, G. Rao, W.E. Bentley: *Biotechnol. Bioeng.,* 75(1), 100, (2001).

[12] D.G. Kang, J.Y.H. Kim, H.J. Cha: *Biotech. Letters*, 24, 879 (2002).

[13] F.P.Goloubinof, A.A.Gatenby, G.H.Lorimer: *Nature*, 337, 44 (1989).

[14] E.I.Rainina, E.N.Efremenco, S.D.Varfolomeev, A.L.Simonian, J.R.Wild: *Biosens. & Bioelectron.,* 11, 991 (1996).

[15] *Russian Federation Patent Application # 2002131715* (2002).

[16] M.-P.Castanié, H.Bergès, J.Oreglia, M.-F. Prère, O. Fayet: *Anal. Biochem.*, 254, 150 (1997).

[17] G.A.Omburo, J.M.Kuo, L.S.Mullins, F. M.Raushel: *J. Biol. Chem.*, 267, 13278 (1992).

In: Biocatalytic Technology and Nanotechnology
Editor: G. E. Zaikov, pp. 73-81
ISBN 1-59454-117-5

Chapter 7

EXPERIENCE WITH APPLICATION OF BIOPREPARATION "RHODER" FOR REMEDIATION OF OIL POLLUTED POLAR MARSHY WETLAND IN KOMI REPUBLIC

Valentina P. Mouryguina and Sergey V. Kalyuzhny

Moscow State University, Chemical Faculty, Chemical Enzymology Dept., Leninskie Gory, 1 Moscow, 119992, Russia

Fax: + 7(095)939-5714, e-mail: vpm@enzyme.chem.msu.ru

ABSTRACT

This paper describes the results of biopreparation "Rhoder" testing on different types of oil-contaminated soils in laboratory, pilot and field trials (both in Komi Republic) during 2001-2003. In laboratory experiments soil was artificially contaminated with crude oil, diesel (both about 10% w/w) or black mineral oil (about 1% w/w). After 5 consecutive treatments with "Rhoder", the initial level of crude oil, diesel and black mineral oil decreased by 57-64%, 54-67%, and 30-72%, respectively, depending on type of structuring agent used (peat or sand). Following phytoremediation with Gramineae seeds decreased the concentration of crude oil and diesel by 10-35% and 15-20 %, respectively. In Komi Republic, during 2001-2003, comparative pilot and field tests of several bioremediation technologies were performed on vast polar marshy wetland soils, which were polluted by accidental crude oil spills. After application of our bioremediation technology with preparation "Rhoder" on the site (2000 m^2) during cold and rainy summer in 2002 (1.5 months), the level of oil contamination decreased by 21-51% depending on the initial oil pollution (458-738 g/kg dry weight of soil). In the middle of September 2002, the treated marshy site was covered with green grass by 70-85%. In the end of August 2003, the treated marshy site was covered with green grass by 85-95% and the level of oil contamination decreased by 40-57% without additional application of "Rhoder" in 2003.

Key words: oil, pollution, oil-degradation microorganisms, preparation, bioremediation, phytoremediation.

1. INTRODUCTION

Accidental oil spills represent one of the major threats for environment in modern society. Among various clean up technologies used nowadays, bioremediation is considered as an economic and efficient method, especially for low contaminated sites. However, conventional bioremediation based on activation of indigenous hydrocarbon-oxidizing bacteria have several limitations dealing with spill age, oil pollution level, local climatic and geological conditions etc. and are generally regarded as a low rate method. To enhance the biodegradation rate, a variety of preparations containing ex-situ produced HCO were proposed and put on market during last decades. We developed one of such preparations called "Rhoder". It was successfully tested in the Western Siberia on various types of oil contaminated wetlands, marshy soils and water surfaces during 1995-2000 [1,2]. In 2001-2002, this preparation was applied for bioremediation of oil contaminated soils in the Polar region in Komi Republic. Harsh geological and climatic conditions in this region impel the company "Lukoil" to search for the most effective and economically sound bioremediation technologies for restoration of vast oil polluted territories. To this end, "Lukoil" organized the comparative testing of several oil-degrading preparations and bioremediation technologies. This paper describes the results of testing of the biopreparation "Rhoder" on different types of oil-contaminated soils in laboratory, pilot and field trials during 2001-2003.

2. EXPERIMENTS, MATERIALS AND METHODS

2.1. Experimental Design

2.1.1 Laboratory Experiments

Lawn-and-garden soil from Moscow region was artificially contaminated with crude oil, diesel (both about 10% w/w) or black mineral oil (about 1% w/w). Before contamination, the soil was dried (105 ^{0}C, 1 h), sieved (0.63 mm) and placed into plastic vessels (15x12x5 cm^3). Due to high clay content in this soil, peat (1/3 w/w) or sand (1/2 w/w) was used as a soil-structuring agent. Since the peat had pH 4.6, fast and slow lime was added in the proportion 1:1 (26 g /vessel) and mixed carefully (the added sand did not change pH). All experimental variants were duplicated. Then after oil contamination and thorough mixing, the vessels were placed into hothouse at 20-23^{0}C without natural light. Throughout experiments, the vessels were periodically watered and mixed for intensification of pollutants degradation. The contaminated soils were treated five times by the suspension of "Rhoder" and fertilizer. The soil samples were taken before each treatment. The soils in control variants were not treated with preparation. Between fourth and fifth treatments with "Rhoder", the phytoremediation was performed during one and a half month with a combination of annual and perennial Gramineae seeds (16.5 g/vessel) previously treated with an anti-stress agent. Phytoremediation was effected under natural light and ambient temperature with regular watering but without sampling. All grasses and ungerminated seeds were pulled out of vessels after terminated the phytoremediation. The final samples were taken to determine the residual hydrocarbons. Soils in the experimental vessels were treated with preparation "Rhoder" once more (fifth) time.

2.1.2. Pilot Test

The pilot tests were performed in 2001 on the accidental (in 1994) oil polluted wetland and sand sites (polluted in 1996) near the town of Usinsk, Komi Republic. Wetland and sand sites were divided in equal plots (3 m x 1m) with wooden pegs and one plot of each site (by lots casting) was designated to evaluate a performance of preparation "Rhoder". Several yeas ago on oil-polluted wetland, drainage-systems (about 1.5 m of wide and depth) were made. In 2000, this wetland was tilled on the depth of about 30 cm and, in 2001 it was very dry and covered with a layer of resembling resinous-asphaltene hydrocarbons. The depth of oil-polluted peat was usually 7 - 10 cm (somewhere about 15-20 cm). No any plants were observed there. pH of peat was about 6.0. The initial concentration of petroleum hydrocarbons was very high (785-900 g/kg dry weight of peat) on this site. Peat deposit had a depth up to 1.3 - 2.2 m and composed of half-decayed sphagnum and sedge-sphagnum peat. On the second sandy site, the upper layer of oil-contaminated sand was taken away and the initial concentration of oil was 82–87 g/kg dry sand. Both plots were dug by spade on the depth of 15-20 cm and lime was added (400 g/plot). Each plot was treated twice with preparation "Rhoder" and fertilizer. The local annual and perennial Gramineae seeds were sowed simultaneously with the first treatment of "Rhoder". The weather was cold (+6 ... + 13^{0}C) and windy, occasional showers during June-August 2001 and only September was warmer then usual.

2.1.3. Field Test

The field test was performed in 2002 on the accidentally oil polluted wetland in Polar region in a cold and humid zone of high northern taiga in Komi Republic. The peat deposit had a maximum depth up to 4.0 m with the upper part up to 1.0-2.0 m, composed of half-decayed (20-30% decay) lowland sedge peat. The low levels of peat deposit were built up with sedge-wood and dead-wood (25-40% decay). The crude oil spilled several times within the last 8-10 years on this marshy surface. There was a complete death of flora in this oil-contaminated wetland. The depth of oil contamination varied from 15 to 25 cm (somewhere to 40 cm). The pH of peat was 4.5-6.0. The area was divided into 9 sites (~2000 m^2 each). Site for evaluation of preparation "Rhoder" performance was given by casting of lots. Our site (total size 25 m x 80 m) was situated on a southwestern part of oil-contaminated wetland. Down of site perimeter, there were made drainage-systems about 1.5 –2.0 m wide and deep. This experimental site was situated near two ponds planed to fill the upper layer of high oil contaminated peat (more then 900 g oil per 1 kg dry peat). Previously this 5-7 cm upper layer of oil-contaminated peat was cut off and moved to the site border. Practically crude oil from border spillad a little bit under sunshine. Only in September 2002, this oil contaminated peat was collected and transported into the slam-ponds. The initial concentration of petroleum hydrocarbons varied from 458 to 738 g/kg dry weight of peat on this site. Each site was twice tilled by ponton-stepped-machine on a depth of 30 cm and lime was added (200 kg/site) without tilling into soil because of impassable wetland. The analysis of soil pH showed that the lime added on experimental site was insufficient. So, the same quantity of lime was added on the site to adjust the soil pH to 7.0. The experimental site was treated three times with preparation "Rhoder" suspension and fertilizer by a sprinkling vacuum pump machinery. Before the second treatment with "Rhoder", a biosorbent (~ 4 kg on 0.02 ha of soil) was put on some pieces of crude oil left after tilling the site. Before the third treatment with "Rhoder", the local annual and perennial Gramineae seeds (oats and timothy-grass 15 and 6 kg respectively) were sowed by hand. Previously all seeds were activated by mixing with an anti-stress agent (4 mL for all seeds) to increase the efficacy of phytoremediation. The weather was unfavorable for bioremediation and active oil degradation by the "Rhoder" microorganisms. At the beginning of the work (in the second and third decades of June 2002) it was cold (+6 - + 10^0C), raining and windy. It was permafrost under a depth of 20-25 cm of oil-contaminated peat. The warm weather (about + 30^0C) with soil temperature about 11-14^0C was only during 10-12 days in mid July. Then it was raining and cold again. During summer 2003 this site was not treated with preparation "Rhoder" at all, but fertilizer (15 kg) was added and timothy-grass (5 kg) were sowed in some bare spots at the beginning of July.

2.2 Materials and Methods

The preparation "Rhoder" (Certificate No 77.99.04.515Д.004855.08.01 issued by Russia Ministry of Health) consists of two Rhodococcus oil degrading strains and represents a concentrated suspension of alive bacterial cells with 10^9 to 10^{10} cells/ml, ready for the application without a preliminary activation [1,2]. The working suspension of "Rhoder" for treatment contained 10^6-10^7 oil degrading cells + Fertilizer (0.2% solution) N_{60}:P_{60}:K_{90} for lab. experiments and N_{15}:P_{15}:K_{15} for pilot and field tests. The polluted soils were treated two times per month during 1.5 –2 months. The samples for analyses were taken before each treatment and 0.5-1 month after last treatment according to 5 points scheme [1]. The level of hydrocarbon pollution was determined by the gravimetric method. Numbers of microorganisms in the treated soils were estimated by MPN method, using the meat-pepton agar for heterotrophic bacteria (HB) and Raymond's liquid medium with oil for hydrocarbon-oxidizing bacteria (HCO) [3]. Soluble nitrogen and phosphorus in soil, humidity and pH were determined by standard agrochemical methods [4]. The seeds of oats, timothy and ribbon grass (60, 12 and 12 g per 1 experimental plot, respectively), were sown in 2001. In 2002, the seeds of oats and timothy-grass (16 and 5 kg per 0.2 ha, respectively) were sown on the experimental wetland site. In 2003m, dry fertilizer (≈20 kg/site) was added without any treatment with "Rhoder" in Polar experimental site. Yet, 15 kg of fertilizer were added and 5 kg timothy-grass were sown in some bare spots at the beginning of July.

3. Results and Discussion

3.1. Laboratory Trials

The laboratory experiment showed that the initial level of crude oil, diesel and black mineral oil decreased by 57-64%, 54-67%, and 72-30%, respectively, after 5 consecutive treatments with "Rhoder" (Table 1). Phytoremediation decreased the concentration of crude oil and diesel by 18-50% and 25-30 %, respectively, depending on peat or sand used as the structuring agent. No influence of phytoremediation was observed for black mineral oil variants (Table 1). The growth of plants was better with a peat as the structuring agent. Preparation "Rhoder" degraded hydrocarbons of crude oil, diesel and black mineral oil efficiently during the first three or four introductions. Then, probably, after the bioavailable hydrocarbons have been exhausted, the oil degradation process became slower in spite of substantial quantity of oil-oxidizing microorganisms, soluble nitrogen and phosphorus, optimal humidity and pH in the soil. The peat and sand used as the structuring agents for clay soil contaminated by hydrocarbons were equally efficient in the case of bioremediation with "Rhoder". The peat as the structuring agent showed a high efficacy especially when it was added to the black mineral oil contaminated soil, perhaps, due to humic substances presented in the peat. The peat humic substances are considered to promote assimilation of difficult access polycyclic hydrocarbons [5]. At the same time, sand as the structuring agent of oil polluted clay soil increased the level of bioremediation especially with the combination of fourfold "Rhoder" treatments and the phytoremediation (Table 1).

3.2. Pilot Trials

During these trials (Table 2.) in Komi Republic, the "Rhoder" decreased THC concentration of oil contaminated peat and sand by 75% and 38%, respectively, and it was selected as one of three most promising Russian preparations for bioremediation of oil spills on polar soils [6]. In summer 2002, there was no any treatment with "Rhoder" in pilot experiment at all, except sampling for analysis of THC concentration. The results obtained showed decrease of oil polluted on the sandy site only (Table 2).

3.3. Field Trials

In spite of high concentration of petroleum hydrocarbons (from 458 to 738 g/kg dry soil) on the "Rhoder" site before remediation, the significant concentrations of indigenous microorganisms ($3.8 \cdot 10^4$ and $1.4 \cdot 10^6$cells/g dry soil of HCO and HT, respectively) were observed as well as the concentrations of soluble nitrogen and phosphorus at 26-37g and 567-687 g/kg dry soil, respectively. According of our technology, some pieces of crude oil remained after tilling were covered with biosorbent to improve bioavailability. After threefold applications of "Rhoder" and the seeding of local annual and perennial Gramineae seeds on the experimental site, the level of oil contamination decreased by 21-51% depending on initial concentration of oil contamination in 2002 and additionally by 10-23% (total 40-57%) in 2003 without treatment of "Rhoder" (Fig.1). Most probably number (MPN) of HCO and HT bacteria during the bioremediation was rather high and decreased a little at the turn of August 2003 during phytoremediation (Fig.2). The humidity of soil was very high 75-81% throughout bioremediation. The soil pH was optimal (6.8 - 7.0) after adding the lime. Nitrogen and phosphorus were assimilated by 90-95% (from the added quantity of fertilizer). In mid September, the treated marshy site was covered with green grass by 70-85%. The biological activity of bioremediated soil was one of the most high among bioremediation technologies tested on the polar marshy wetland. The results obtained showed that the preparation

Table 1. Laboratory trials. Degradation of hydrocarbon contamination by preparation "Rhoder"

Variants		THC, g/kg							Total degradation %
		Before treatment	14 days after the 1st treatment	14 days after the 2nd treatment	14 days after the 3rd treatment	14 days after the 4th treatment	After phytoremediation	14 days after the 5th treatment	
Crude oil, 10%	Peat	33.10	28.81	19.73	19.50	19.78	16.15	14.20	57.1
	Sand	48.43	33.45	37.60	33.50	32.02	15.22	17.52	63.8
	Without treatment	61.26	55.98	55.70	54.90	55.0	54.78	53.80	12.2
Diesel, 10%	Peat	36.03	38.43	31.14	28.11	22.00	16.60	16.58	54.0
	Sand	49.72	49.63	43.37	37.33	30.96	20.64	16.38	67.1
	Without treatment	61.02	65.06	64.70	60.40	57.49	52.10	51.79	15.1
Black Mineral oil, 1%	Peat	11.0	10.09	6.58	3.77	2.78	2.64	3.02	72.5
	Sand	6.39	6.18	4.83	3.32	4.40	5.22	4.27	30.9
	Without treatment	7.50	7.65	7.04	7.39	7.12	7.45	7.00	6.7

Table 2. Pilot trials. Bioremediation of oil contaminated wetland and sandy soils in Usinsk, Komi Republic, 2001-2002

Object	2001			2002	
	THC concentration, g/kg		Degradation, %	THC, g/kg,	Degradation, %
	Start	End			
WETLAND (oil spill in 1994)					
Control without any treatment	904.0	975.0	0	879.5	9.8
2 treatments **with "Rhoder"**	911.5	224.6	75.4	232.4	70.7
SANDY SOIL (oil spill in 1996)					
Control without any treatment	87.0	89.1	0	72.6	16.2
2 treatments **with "Rhoder"**	87.0	53.6	38.4	30.4	65.0

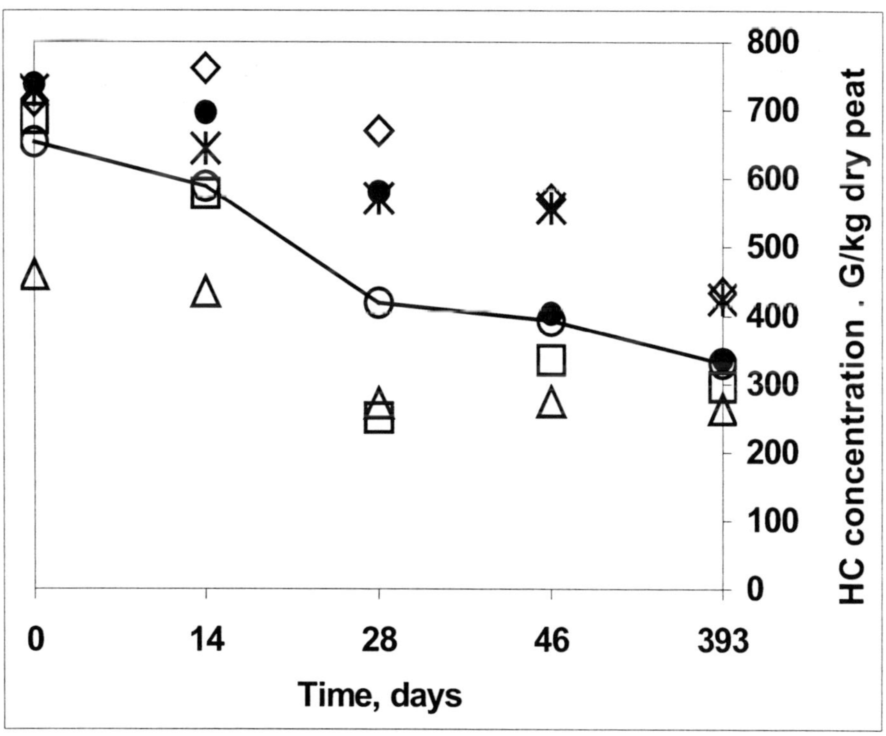

Fig. 1. Decrease of HC concentration during the bioremediation with the preparation "Rhoder"

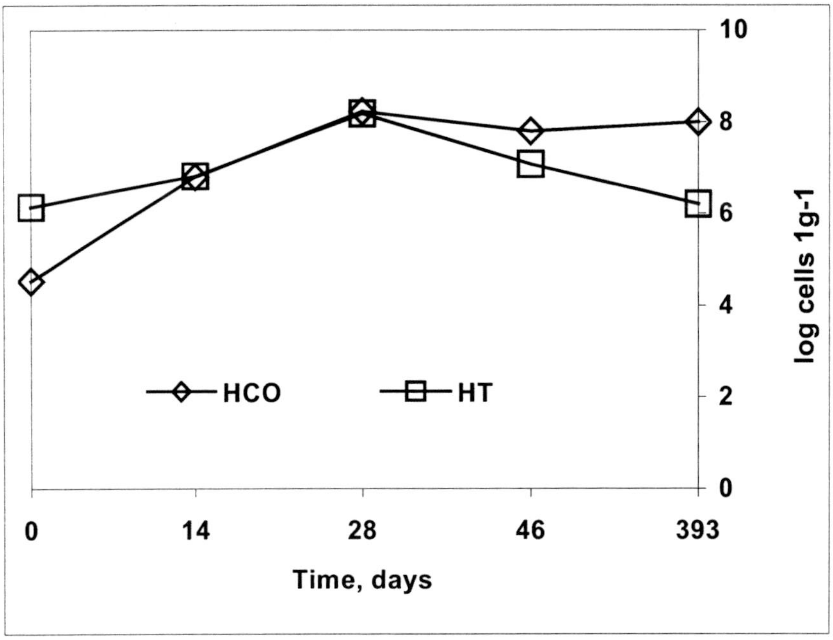

Fig. 2. Microorganism counts during bioremediation with the preparation "Rhoder"

"Rhoder" can be efficiently used even on the sites with extremely high oil pollution, but, in this case, it is not expected that the bioremediation will be finished during one season without additional treatment contaminated soil with the preparation "Rhoder". In the end of August 2003, the treated marshy site was covered with green grass by 85-95%.

4. Conclusions

The results obtained during laboratory, pilot and field trails in 2001-2002 showed that the preparation "Rhoder" can degrade crude oil, diesel and black mineral oil by 40-70% after three or four consecutive applications under the hydrocarbon concentrations from 10-100 g/kg to 750 g/kg dry soil even if the weather is unfavorable for bioremediation in Polar region. Introduction of "Rhoder" in 2002 and following the phytoremediation in 2003 decreased oil contamination by 40-57% during two warm seasons in Polar region in Komi Republic.

Acknowledgements

The authors wish to thank the company Lukoil for financial support of this work, FGUP NIPI "Komimeliowodkhozproekt" for assistance with field trials, Dr. Irina Perminova for biosorbent delivery, Salem Qayid for technical assistance.

REFERENCES

[1] V.P. Murygina, M.U. Arinbasarov, S.V. Kalyuzhnyi: *Biodegradation*, 11 (6), 385 (2000).

[2] V.P. Mouryguina, S.V. Kalyuzhny: *Proc. of the First European Bioremediation Conference*, 3-5 June, Crete, Greece, 28 (2001).

[3] T. Nazina, Ye. Rozanova, S. Belyayev, M. Ivanov: "*Chemical and microbiological methods of investigation of liquid and solid samples from oil fields*". Biological Center Press, Pushchino, 1988. 35 p (in Russian)

[4] E. Durynina, V. Egoroff: *Agrochemical analysis of soil, plants, fertilizer*. MSU Moscow, 1998. 147 p (in Russian).

[5] V. Kholodov, N. Kulikova, I. Perminova: *Proc. of NATO Advanced Research Workshop*. September 23-29, Zvenigorod, Russia, 22 (2002).

[6] A. Alexandrov, V. Zagvozdkin, G. Ertzev, et.al.: *Proc. Inetrn. Confer. of ICS and UNIDO "New Technologies for Clean up Oil Contaminated Waters and Soils, remaking and use Oil-Slimes"*., 10-11 of December, Moscow, 96 (2001).

In: Biocatalytic Technology and Nanotechnology
Editor: G. E. Zaikov, pp. 83-91
ISBN 1-59454-117-5

Chapter 8

APPLICATION OF MICROBIAL CELLS FOR TRANSFORMATION OF NUCLEOSIDES INTO NUCLEOSIDE-5'-DIPHOSPHATES

O. I. Titovich, S. V. Kvach, V. N. Barai, I. A. Mikhailopulo and A. I. Zinchenko

Institute of Microbiology, National Academy of Sciences, 220141 Minsk, Acad. Kuprevicha 2, Belarus. E-mail: zinch@mbio.bas-net.by; fax: +375(172)64-47-66

ABSTRACT

A one-pot two-step enzymatic method for the synthesis of natural and sugar- and base-modified nucleoside-5'-diphosphates (NDP's) is suggested. The method consists of an enzymatic consecutive transformation of nucleoside-5'-monophosphates (NMP's) into their nucleoside-5'-triphosphates (NTP's) under conditions of glucose glycolytic cleavage and then (without isolation of NTP's from the reaction mixture) into NDP's employing baker's yeast as a biocatalyst. An improved method for an enzymatic synthesis of NMP's using nucleoside phosphotransferase (NPase) of the whole cells of *Erwinia herbicola* as a biocatalyst is described.

Keywords: nucleoside; nucleoside-5'-monophosphate; nucleoside-5'-diphosphate; enzymatic transformation; *Saccharomyces cerevisiae*; nucleoside phosphotransferase; *Erwinia herbicola*

1. INTRODUCTION

Naturally occurring and sugar- and base-modified NMP's and NDP's are valuable compounds for different biochemical and molecular biological studies (see, *e.g.*, [1-3]). The natural NMP's can be obtained by microbial synthesis or by isolation from nucleic acids, which are the main natural sources of these compounds [4]. Methods for the synthesis of modified NMP's are based either on chemical [2, 5] or on an enzymatic phosphorylation of corresponding nucleosides [6-9]. Natural and modified NDP's have been usually synthesized by chemical methods [2, 5].

It is well known that the NMP yields obtained by chemical phosphorylation of modified nucleosides are varied in a wide range depending on a method employed, the structure of initial compounds, and from assay to assay as well. On the other hand, the enzymatic approach to a 5'-monophosporylation seems to be advantageous over the chemical methods. The reactions of enzymatic 5'-monophosphorylation are, however, either reversible or they are inhibited by the reaction products, NMP's, which necessitates one to use a phosphate donor in manifold molar excess *vs.* a nucleoside [6, 7, 9, 10]. Microbial and plant NPase (EC 2.7.1.77) are most widely applied as biocatalysts for 5'-monophosphorylation of nucleosides. As distinct from nucleoside kinases, these enzymes show a much more broad specificity with respect to phosphate donors and acceptors, and they can use as substrate low-energy monoesthers of phosphoric acid such as, *e.g.*, NMP's and *p*-nitrophenylphosphate (*p*-PNP).

In the present paper previously described method for the preparation of NMP's using the whole cells *Erw. herbicola* 47/3 [7, 9] as a biocatalyst, was improved by an application of Zn^{2+} ions for the precipitation of NMP's from the phosphorylating mixture during the course of reaction. Moreover, we have investigated the synthesis of NDP's from NMP's employing kinase system of *Sacch. cerevisiae* (baker's yeast). This transformation includes the consecutive transformation of NMP's into NTP's upon glycolysis (*cf.*, *e.g.*, [7], followed by high-selective monodephosphorylation under carefully selected conditions.

2. Materials and Methods

Reagents

Adenosine (Ado) and *p*-NPP were purchased from Sigma (USA). Silufol UV_{254} aluminum sheets for thin layer chromatography (TLC) were obtained from Serva (Germany). 1-(β-D-arabinofuranosyl)cytosine (ara-Cyd) and 1-(β-D-arabinofuranosyl)uracil (ara-Urd) were purchased from Fluka (Germany). Preparation of 9-(β-D-arabinofuranosyl)guanine (ara-Guo) was described previously [11]. Syntheses of 9-(β-D-arabinofuranosyl)adenine (ara-Ado), 9-(β-D-arabinofuranosyl)-2-aminoadenine (ara-2-NH_2-Ado) and 9-(β-D-arabinofuranosyl)-2-fluoroadenine (ara-2-F-Ado) were realized by enzymatic transglycosylation as it is described for preparation of base- and sugar-modified nucleosides in [12]. The purity of all compounds was checked by TLC and high-performance liquid chromatography (HPLC), and the structure was proved by ^{1}H NMR spectroscopy.

The UV spectra were recorded in ethanol on a Specord M-400 spectrometer (Carl Zeiss, Germany). HPLC was carried out with the Waters apparatus (Waters, USA); column Nova-Pac C-18 (3.9 × 300 mm) (Waters); and an isocratic elution with the following buffer: 7% CH_3CN in 0.1 M KH_2PO_4, v/v) at a flow rate 0.7 ml/min (time of analysis was 15 min).

Microorganisms

Erwinia herbicola 47/3 cells were grown in 250-ml flasks containing 50 ml of the following medium (mg/ml): 6.0 Na_2HPO_4; 3.0 KH_2PO_4; 0.5 NaCl; 1.0 NH_4CL; 0.12 $MgSO_4$; 3.0 Sigma (USA) meat peptone; 5.0 Serva (Germany) yeast extract. The initial pH of the culture medium was adjusted to 7.0. Cultivation was carried out on a circular shaker (180-200 rpm) at 28°C for 24 h. Biomass was harvested by centrifugation (4500 g, 10 min), washed twice with two volumes of 0.85% (w/v) NaCl, estimated by weighing an aliquot after drying at 105°C for 24 h, and suspended in a small volume of the same solution.

Commercially available baker's yeast used for the preparation of NDP's have been dried at 28°C for 24 h.

Standard Reaction Conditions for Enzymatic Synthesis of NMP's

The reaction mixture (3 ml) consisted of 30 mM nucleoside, 90 mM *p*-NPP, 0.2 M sodium acetate buffer (pH 4.5), 0.1 M salt of cation studied and wet paste of bacterial cells (1%, w/v; calculated as abs. dry weight). The mixture was incubated at 37°C with gentle stirring. Aliquots of the reaction medium were diluted twice with 0.25 M EDTA (pH 7.5) and analyzed by TLC as described [Zinchenko *et al.* 1990].

Preparative Synthesis of NMP's

In the case of preparative (10-ml scale) NMP's synthesis, after the reaction was completed, the pH of reaction medium was adjusted to 7.0 with 1 M NaOH. The mixture was heated to 80°C and centrifuged (5000 g, 10 min). The sediment obtained was washed with 5 ml of hot (50-60°C) water and dissolved in 8 ml of 0.1 M EDTA (pH 7.0), then the cells were removed by centrifugation and washed with 2 ml of 0.1 M EDTA (pH 7.0). Two supernatants were combined and NMP was isolated using a procedure described by Rideout et al. [13].

Standard Reaction Conditions for Enzymatic Synthesis of NDP's

At the first stage, commercially available baker's yeast has been used for the transformation of NMP's into corresponding NTP's. The reaction mixture (10 ml) consisting of 40 mM NMP or adenosine (Ado), glucose (2%), 15 mM $MgCl_2$, 0.2-0.3 M potassium phosphate buffer (pH 7.0), and dry yeast cells (10%) was incubated at 20-28°C under gentle stirring for 2-7 h. Progress of the synthesis was monitored by TLC.

At the second stage (in the case of pyrimidine NDP's preparation), inorganic pyrophosphate (PPi; final concentration 30 mM) and NaF (final concentration 10 mM) were added to a reaction mixture and the mixture was stirred for 80-100 min at 55°C.

In the case of purine NDP's preparation, the pH of the reaction mixture was adjusted to 3.0 by 2 M HCl and the cells were separated by centrifugation (5000 g; 5 min). The pH of supernatant was adjusted to 5.5-7.0 with 1 M NaOH, dry yeast (0.2-0.6%) and glucose (final concentration 1%) were added and the mixture was stirred at 55°C for 60-80 min.

3. Results

Synthesis of NMP's

At the first stage, we studied the bivalent metal ions, which can form water-insoluble salts with AMP and *p*-NPP in the standard reaction medium (without biocatalyst). Among ions studied (Ba^{2+}, Ca^{2+}, Cu^{2+}, Co^{2+}, Zn^{2+}, and Ni^{2+}), only Zn^{2+} and Cu^{2+} have shown the ability to precipitate AMP and, to a much lesser extent, *p*-NPP (see Table 1). The higher solubility of the corresponding salts of *p*-NPP is rather important because its precipitation would essentially slow down the desired transformation. The results of AMP synthesis are presented in Table 1.

Table 1. Effect of bivalent metal ions on solubility of AMP and *p*-NPP, and efficiency of AMP synthesis by the *Erw. herbicola* cells as well

Added salt in the medium	Solubility (mM)		Max. degree of Ado conversion to AMP (mol.%)	Time of attaining max. conversion (h)
	AMP	*P*-NPP		
$CuCl_2$	0.42	25.1	65	6
$ZnCl_2$	0.17	12.2	83	6
None	*)	*)	60	13

*) Precipitate was not formed.

It is obvious from the data shown in Table 1 that both cations, Zn^{2+} and Cu^{2+}, increase the AMP yield along with the considerable decrease of the reaction time. Taking into account that Zn^{2+} displayed higher efficiency *vs.* Cu^{2+}, further experiments have been carried out using $ZnCl_2$.

Thus, on the example of Ado phosphorylation by *Erw. herbicola* NPase we have demonstrated the possibility to increase the yield of AMP synthesis from 60 up to 83% with a simultaneous decrease (almost in two times) of reaction durability due to the presence of zinc ions in the reaction medium.

At the next stage, we have studied the efficiency of the base- and sugar-modified NMP's synthesis employing the conditions for the AMP synthesis (Table 2). In all (except for one) examples studied, we have observed improvement of the yield of NMP's in the presence of Zn^{2+} ions. In our opinion, this fact denotes a shift in the equilibrium state of the reaction to the formation of NMP's (principal products) due to their precipitation in the form of water-insoluble salts. This assumption is corroborated by the fact that Zn^{2+} ions do not affect the yield of ara-Urd transformation into ara-UMP; the latter lacks the ability to form insoluble residue with Zn^{2+} ions under reaction conditions.

Synthesis of NDP's

We have earlier shown that cells of baker's yeast are able to transform natural and modified NMP's into NTP's upon glycolysis [7]. Along with the NTP's formation, the presence of the corresponding NDP's was observed that have been isolated from the reaction mixtures in some cases, and their structure was proved by spectral methods. Detailed investigation of the CMP → CTP transformation showed that CDP emerged mainly from CTP. It was further observed that the rising of temperature of the reaction mixture from 20°C to 55°C after completion of the CMP → CTP transformation led to the partial dephosphorylation of the latter affording CDP as the principal product (Table 3).

Table 2. Effect of Zn^{2+} ions on solubility of NMP's and efficiency of NMP synthesis by the *Erw. herbicola* cells

Initial nucleoside	NMP solubility (mM)	Max. degree of nucleoside conversion to NMP (mol.%)		Time of attaining max. conversion (h)	
	$+Zn^{2+}$	$-Zn^{2+}$	$+Zn^{2+}$	$-Zn^{2+}$	$+Zn^{2+}$
Ara-Ado	0.15	36	59	11	12
Ara-2-F-Ado	0.14	33	55	11	12
Ara-2-NH_2-Ado	0.17	35	58	11	12
Ara-Guo	2.8	32	41	7	8
Ara-Cyd	3.6	26	42	7	8
Ara-Urd*)	30.0	29	27	6	6
2-NH_2-Ado	0.19	65	91	8	7

*) Precipitate was not formed.

Table 3. Quantitative analysis of the reaction mixtures of optimal CMP → CTP transformation and then complete CTP → CDP transformation

Components of the reaction mixture	Concentration in the reaction mixture (mol.%)	
	Optimal CMP → CTP transformation	Complete CTP → CDP transformation
Cyd	20.6	19.2
CMP	5.9	10.4
CDP	10.4	70.4
CTP	63.1	0

It is known the cells of baker's yeast contain uridine-5'-diphosphoglucose pyrophosphorylase (UTP:α-D-glucose-1-phosphate uridylyltransferase; EC 2.7.7.9) that catalyses synthesis of uridine-5'-diphosphoglucose (UDPG) from UTP and D-glucoso-1-α-phosphate. Indeed, we have observed the formation of UDPG under glycolytic synthesis of UTP from UMP (Fig. 1). On the other hand, an addition of PPi and NaF to the reaction medium of the UMP → UTP transformation by *Candida sp.* N-25-2, which contains UDPG, results in conversion of UDPG into UTP [14]. Similar results have been observed under our experimental conditions for the UMP → UTP transformation in the presence of *Sacch. cerevisiae* cells.

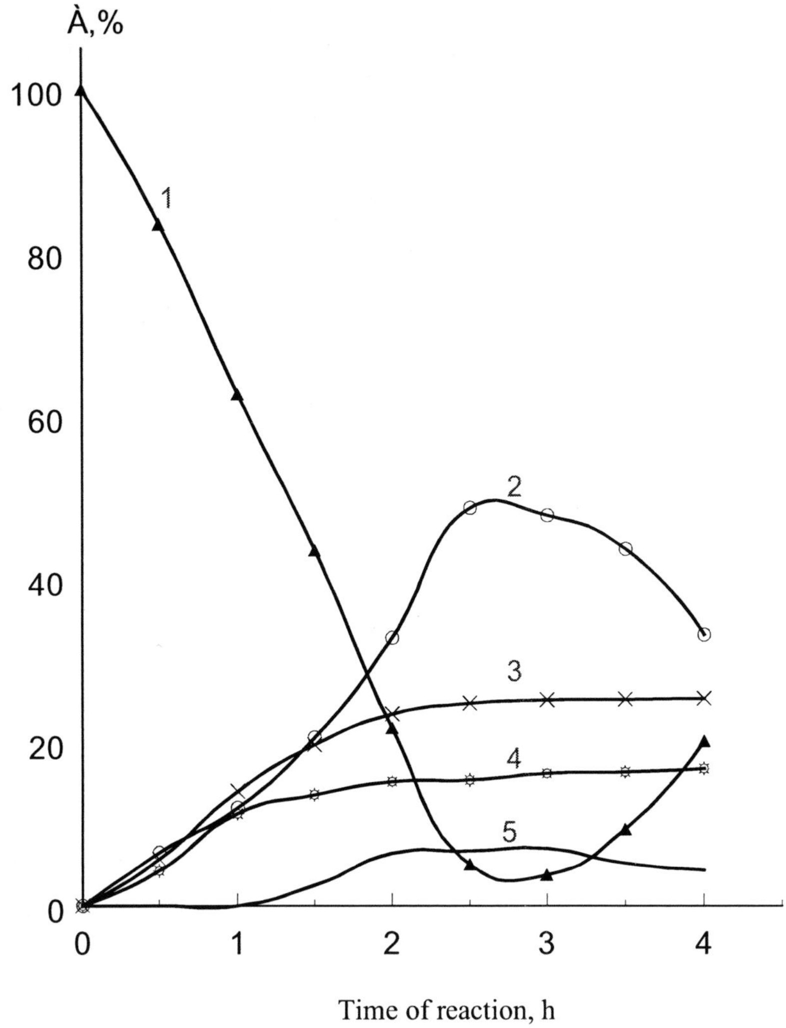

Fig. 1. Dynamics of the formation and degradation of uridine nucleotides during UMP → UTP transformation by baker's yeast cells. 1 – UMP; 2 – UTP; 3 – UDPG; 4 – Urd; 5 – UDP. A – concn, % mol.

More detailed study of the UMP → UTP transformation in the presence of *Sacch. cerevisiae* cells revealed that varying reaction temperature and concentrations of PPi and NaF one can displace the equilibrium to the UDP formation. Indeed, the UMP → UTP transformation in the absence of PPi and NaF led to the formation of UTP along with a marked quantity of UDPG. However, rising temperature of a mixture to 55°C followed by an addition of PPi and NaF led to disappearance of UDPG and a fast transformation of UTP into UDP (Fig. 2).

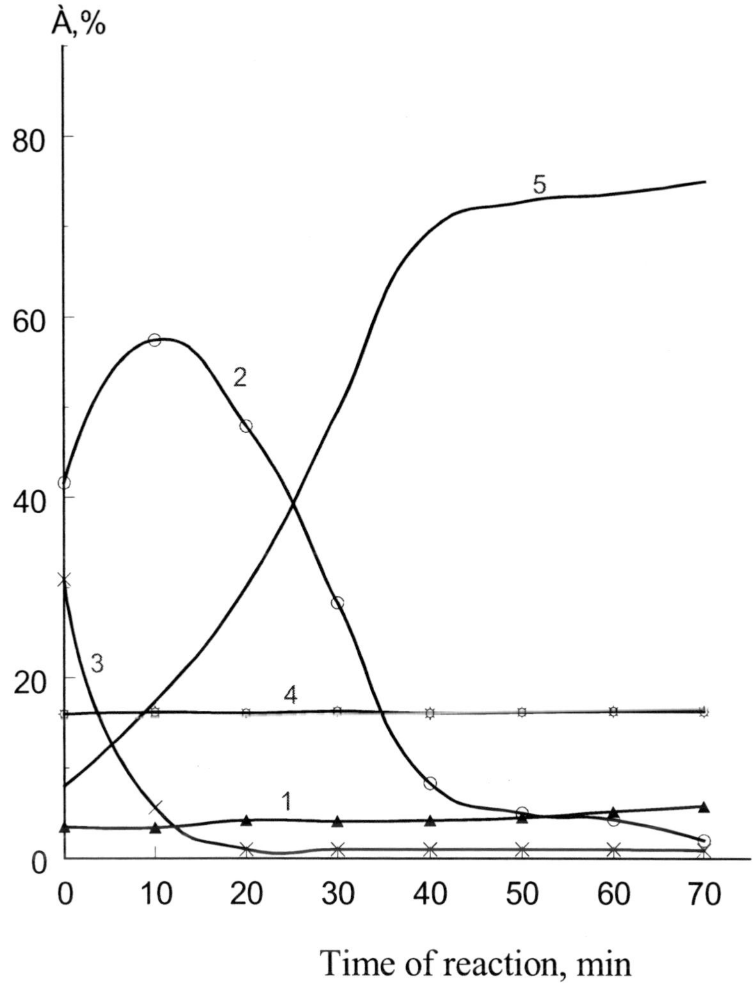

Fig. 2. Dynamics of the formation uridine nucleotides in the presence of PPi and NaF. 1 – UMP; 2 – UTP; 3 – UDPG; 4 – Urd; 5 – UDP. A – concn, % mol.

Transformation of GMP into GTP in the presence of the *Sacch. cerevisiae* cells was found to be accompanied by the formation of small quantity of guanosine-5'-diphosphoglucose (GDPG). An addition of PPi to the reaction mixture after completion of the GTP synthesis led to disappearance of GDPG. However, as distinct from the UDP synthesis, GDP was not the principal product in this case, but further dephosphorylation took place giving rise to GMP and guanosine. Adjusting the pH of the reaction mixture to 2.5-3.0 followed by (i) separation by centrifugation of precipitate formed, (ii) neutralizing the supernatant to pH 7.0, (iii) addition of PPi and dry yeast, and (iv) incubation of the mixture at 55°C for 60-80 min allowed to realize consecutive transformation of GMP → GTP → GDP in a yield of 76%. It is likely that a short term incubation of the reaction mixture at pH 2.5-3.0 led to deactivation of enzymes catalyzing dephosphorylation of GDP and GMP.

In a similar way, Ado was transformed into ATP and then to ADP in 84% yield.

The data on the synthesis of a number of NDP's are presented in Table 4. It is noteworthy that the suggested approach to the synthesis of NDP's from NMP's using the whole cells of *Sacch. cerevisiae* through intermediary formation of NTP's showed rather good effectiveness.

Table 4. Data on the synthesis of some NDP's from NMP's using the whole cells of *Sacch. cerevisiae* through intermediary formation of NTP's

Initial NMP	Combined yield of NTP+NDP (mol.%)	Yield of NDP (mol.%)
dAMP	83	76
dGMP	81	72
dCMP	77	69
dUMP	77	70
2-NH_2-AMP	84	75
ara-(2-NH_2-AMP)	81	71
ara-AMP	85	78
ara-CMP	78	70

4. Conclusion

In conclusion, it should be stressed that the method described in this communication may be used for the rather efficient production of NDP's from natural and base- and sugar-modified nucleosides as well. The method consists of an enzymatic consecutive transformation of NMP's into their NTP's and then, without isolation of NTP's, into NDP's employing commercial baker's yeast (*Sacch. cerevisiae)* as a biocatalyst. An improved method for an enzymatic synthesis of NMP's using NPase of the whole sells of *Erw. herbicola* as a biocatalyst is described.

References

[1] H. Becheur, D. Valla, M. A. Loriot, A. Attar, F. Bloch, J. P. Petite: *Dig. Dis. Sci.*, **43** (11), 2479 (1998).
[2] K. Burgess, D. Cook: *Chem. Rev.,* **100** (6), 2047 (2000).
[3] M. A. Boogaerts, H. A. Van, D. Catovsky et al.: *J. Clin. Oncol.,* **19** (22), 4252 (2001).
[4] K. Ogata et al. (Eds): *Microbial Production of Nucleic Acid-related Substances.* Kodansha Ltd, Tokyo, 75 (1976).
[5] K. H. Scheit: *Nucleotide Analogs: Synthesis and Biological Function.* Wiley-Interscience, New York, 1980. 288 p.
[6] R. W. Humble, G. Mackenzie, G. Shaw: *Nucleosides & Nucleotides*, **3** (4), 363 (1984).
[7] A. I. Zinchenko, V. N. Barai, L. M. Zalashko et al.: *FEBS Lett.,* **260** (2), 254 (1990).
[8] M. Rutkowski, M. Draminski: *Acta Biochim. Pol.*, **38** (4), 449 (1991).
[9] G. V. Zaitseva, E. I. Kvasyuk, E. V. Vaaks et al.: *Nucleosides & Nucleotides*, **13** (1-3), 819 (1994).
[10] J. Giziewicz, D. Shugar: *Acta Biochim. Polon.,* **22** (1), 87 (1975).

[11] A. I. Zinchenko, V. N. Barai, S. B. Bokut et al.: *Appl. Microbiol. Biotechnol.,* **32** (3), 658 (1990).
[12] V. N. Barai, A. I. Zinchenko, L. A. Eroshevskaya et al.: *Helv. Chim. Acta*, **85** (7), 1901 (2002).
[13] J. E. Rideout, R. L. Miller, G. B. Elion: *Pat. US 4136175* (1979)
[14] S. Shiroto, S. Watanabe, I. Takeda: *Agric. Biol. Chem.,* **35** (3), 325 (1971).

In: Biocatalytic Technology and Nanotechnology
Editor: G. E. Zaikov, pp. 93-103
ISBN 1-59454-117-5

Chapter 9

ENZYMATIC SYNTHESIS OF POLYELECTROLYTE COMPLEXES OF CONDUCTING POLYANILINE

Ivan Yu. Sakharov *

Chemical Enzymology Department, Faculty of Chemistry, The M. V. Lomonosov Moscow State University, Bldg. 1/11 Moscow 119992, Russia

ABSTRACT

Enzymatic synthesis of polyelectrolyte complexes of polyaniline (PANI) and sulfonated polystyrene (SPS) was developed. Royal palm tree peroxidase and laccase *Coriolus hirsutus* active and stable under acidic conditions, were used as biocatalysts. The template polymerization of aniline was carried out in aqueous buffer at pH 3.5-3.7. Varying the concentrations of aniline, SPS and hydrogen peroxide in feed, the favorable conditions for production of PANI were determined. Contrary to chemical polymerization of aniline, the enzymatic reaction is controlled kinetically and proceeds under environmentally friendly ("green") conditions.

ABBREVIATIONS

PANI	polyaniline
SPS	sulfonated polystyrene
RPTP	royal palm tree peroxidases
HRP	horseradish peroxidase

* To whom the correspondence should be addressed: Ivan Yu. Sakharov, Ph.D, D.Sc., Department of Chemical Enzymology, Faculty of Chemistry, M.V.Lomonosov Moscow State University, Lenin's Hills, Moscow 119992, Russia, Phone: 7-095-9393407, Fax: 7-095-9392742, E.mail: sakharov@enz.chem.msu.ru

INTRODUCTION

Recent years, there has been a tremendous interest in the production of conducting polymers. Polyaniline (PANI) is one of the most extensively investigated conducting polymers due to its high environmental stability and promising electronic properties. The potential for its use is a wide range of applications including organic lightweight batteries, light-emitting diodes, optical display, anticorrosive protection, bioanalysis, etc. [1-4].

In the course of polymerization of aniline, the emeraldine base of PANI is formed (Scheme 1). The emeraldine base of PANI is not a conductor; only its derivative, emeraldine salt is a conductive form. Emeraldine salt is usually obtained from emeraldine base via protonation of its imine sites with sufficiently strong acids, such as organic sulfonic and phosphoric acids [1]. This process is termed "doping".

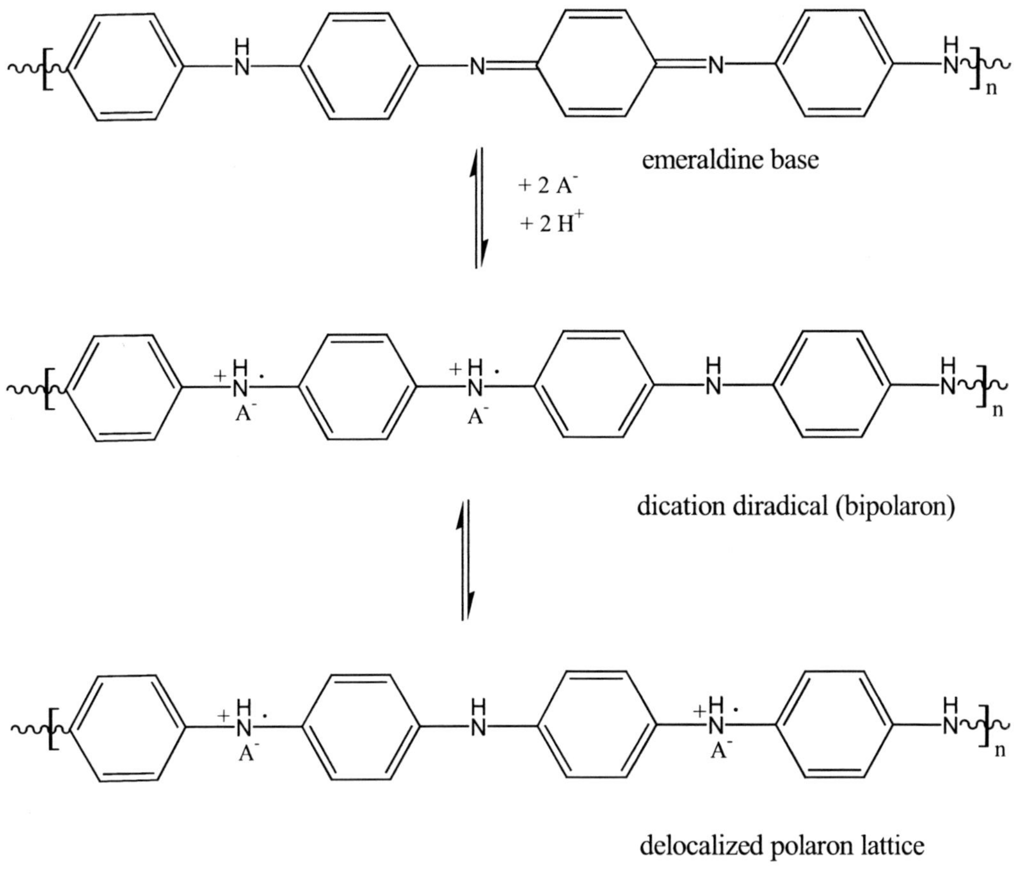

Scheme 1. Chemical structure of polyaniline.

Doped PANI is not processable because of its poor solubility in common solvents [5,6]. Polyelectrolyte complexes of PANI and soluble polymers carrying negatively charged groups form a stable dispersion of nanoparticles in aqueous media and, hence, the processibility of such complexes is higher than that of PANI itself.

The polyelectrolyte complexes of PANI may be produced both chemically and enzymatically. The chemical polymerization of monomer aniline is conducted under strongly acidic conditions [2,7].

Conversely, the enzymatic reaction can be performed under environmentally friendly conditions. The synthesis of polyelectrolyte complexes of PANI catalyzed horseradish peroxidase was reported previously [8,9]. HRP-catalyzed polymerization of monomer aniline was performed in presence of hydrogen peroxide as reducing substrate. Unfortunately, HRP shows the low stability at pH below 4.5 [8,10,11], i.e. at the same pH interval where the polyelectrolyte complex between PANI (pK_a of aniline is 4.63) and negatively charged polymeric templates can be formed. This results in a consumption of a large amount of HRP in polymerization. To develop more technological processes, alternative oxidoreductases capable to effectively polymerize aniline under acidic conditions should be used.

It is well known that laccase can catalyze the oxidation of a lot of inorganic and organic substrates under acidic conditions [12]. Furthermore, novel peroxidases were recently isolated from leaves of African oil palm tree [13] and royal palm tree [14]. These enzymes showed unusual stability at high temperatures and in a abroad pH range [15,16]. This paper reports a detailed investigation on synthesis of conducting SPS-polyaniline complexes using laccase *Coriolus hirsutus* and royal palm tree peroxidase as catalysts as well as some properties of the complexes obtained.

Materials and Methods

Materials

Aniline, Na_2HPO_4 and citric acid were purchased from Sigma Chemical Co. (St. Louis, MO). Commercial aniline was purified by distillation before use. Sulfonated polystyrene (MW 70000) was produced by Aldrich Chemical Co. Inc. (Milwaukee, WI).

Laccase was isolated from the culture fluid of *Coriolus hirsutus*. The procedure for purification was described elsewhere [12]. The specific activity of laccase measured toward catechol was no less than 350 units/mg protein.

Royal palm tree peroxidase was purified to homogeneity as described earlier [14]. The specific activity of the palm peroxidase measured toward guaiacol was 6000 units/mg protein.

The synthesis of SPS-PANI complex was carried out as described previously [17, 18]. Monomer aniline and SPS were dissolved in 0.1 M sodium citrate up to 100 mM and then, the pH value of the reaction medium was adjusted using the concentrated phosphoric acid. The aniline polymerization was evaluated using the UV-Vis spectroscopy (Shimadzu UV-2401 PC spectrophotometer).

Results and Discussion

HRP-catalyzed polymerization of conducting polyaniline is usually conducted at pH ~4.0, which is not the optimal pH for HRP catalysis. Under these conditions, HRP loses its catalytic activity for a very short time period, which results in consumption of a large amount of the enzyme during the polymerization reaction. Since *Coriolus hirsutus* laccase is active and stable under acidic conditions [12], it will have a great advantage compared to HRP in the template-assisted polymerization of aniline.

The laccase-catalyzed polymerization of aniline was studied in the pH range 3.5–4.4. The reaction was carried out at ambient temperature in presence of sulfonated polystyrene (SPS) (Scheme 2), the negatively charged polymer used as template in PANI synthesis. Figure 1 shows a strong polaron absorption band at about 700-780 nm observed at pH 3.5, 3.7 and 3.9 indicating the formation of conducting polyaniline. Therefore, we can conclude that laccase can catalyze the polymerization of aniline in presence of SPS to form polyaniline under mild conditions compared to the traditional chemical method [19,20].

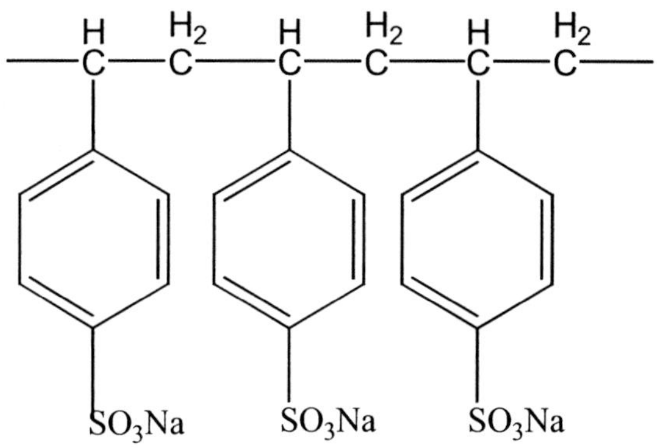

Scheme 2. Chemical structure of sulfonated polystyrene

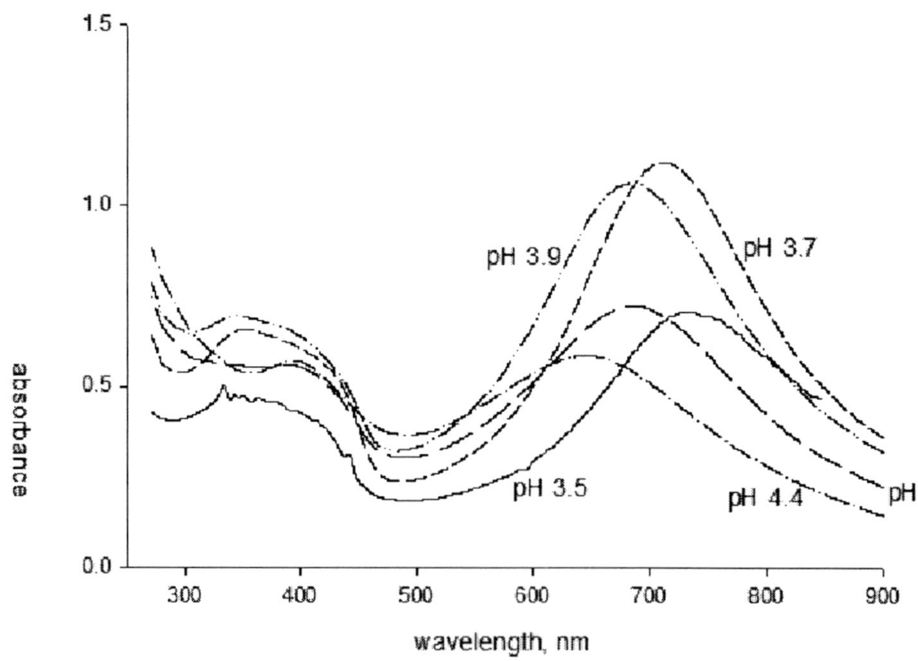

Figure 1. The pH effect on the rate of aniline polymerization in presence of SPS catalyzed by laccase at 20^0C. Experimental conditions: 0.1 M citrate-phosphate buffer; [aniline] = [SPS] = 6 mM; [laccase] = 5.5 x 10^{-7} M; the spectra were recorded 15 min after the polymerization initiation.

Another enzyme, we used in the synthesis of PANI-SPS complexes, was RPTP. Like laccase, RPTP retains the specific activity up to pH 3.0 [14]. The study of the pH effect of the reaction medium on the rate of enzymatic oxidation of aniline showed that the pH-optimum of the reaction is at pH 3.5 (Fig. 2). Therefore, the favorite pH values both for the enzymatic polymerization of aniline by the laccase and RPTP and for the formation of the polyelectrolyte complex are the same.

To evaluate the effect of aniline concentration on the polymerization rate, kinetics of the reaction was studied varying the substrate concentrations 25 mM to 100 mM. Figure 3 shows that the rate of aniline polymerization increases with its concentration in feed.

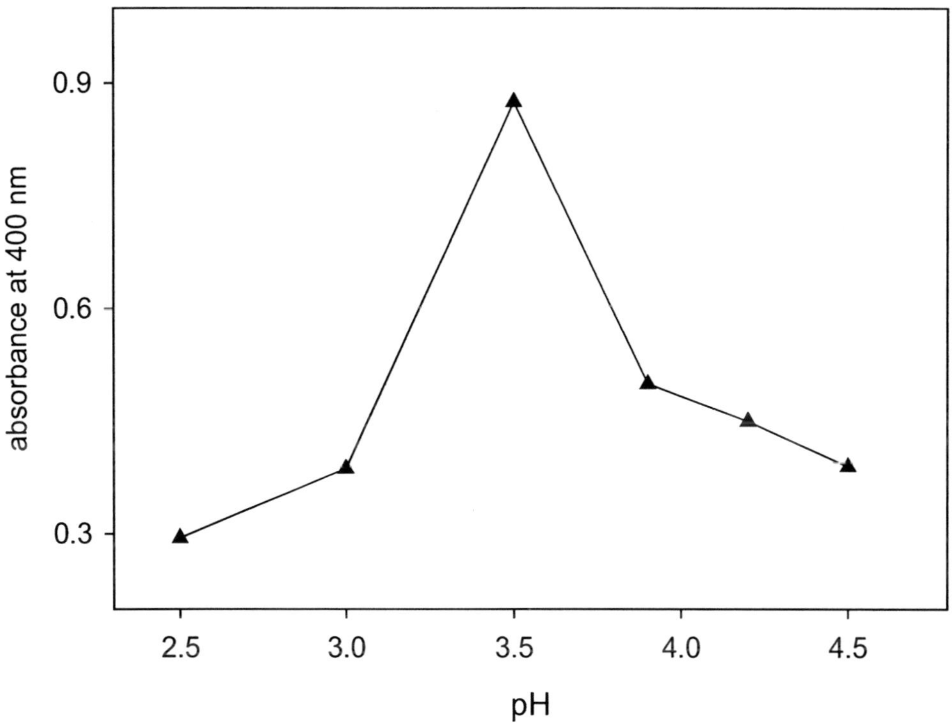

Figure 2. The pH effect on the aniline polymerization rate in presence of SPS catalyzed by royal palm tree peroxidase at 20^0C. Experimental conditions: 0.1 M citrate-phosphate buffer; [aniline] = [SPS] = 20 mM; $[H_2O_2]$ = 4 mM; [RPTP] = 8.6 x 10^{-8} M.

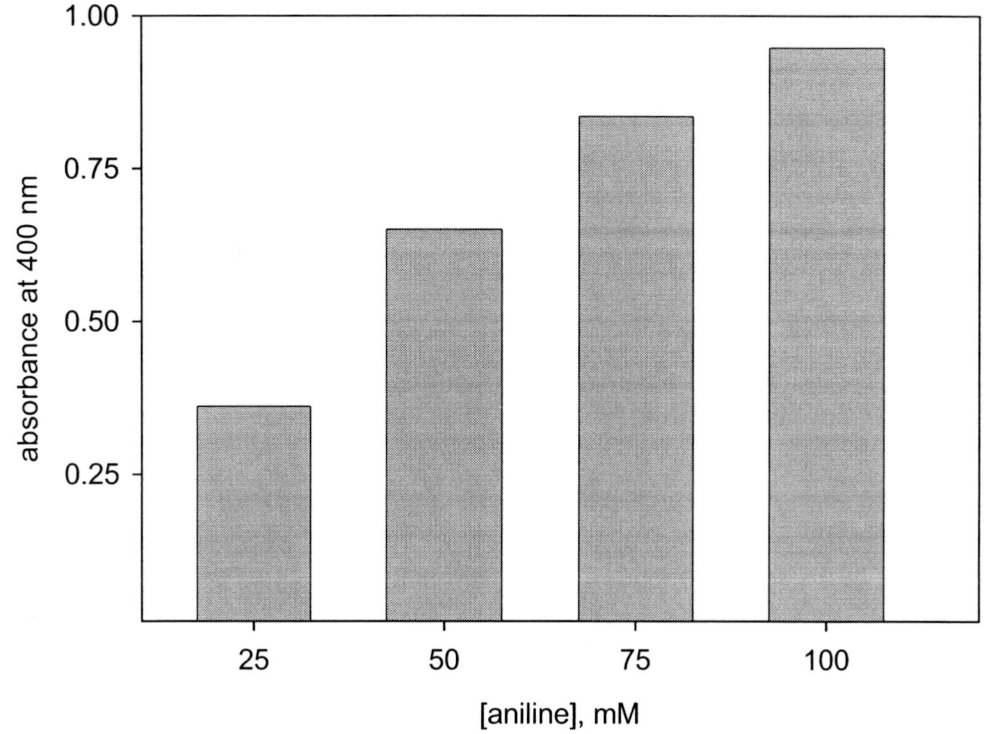

Figure 3. Effect of aniline concentrations on polyaniline enzymatic synthesis rate.

It is to be emphasized that even at high aniline concentrations, the substrate inhibition of RPTP and laccase was not observed, and the preparative synthesis can be conducted with maximal efficiency of the enzyme.

The effect of SPS concentration on polymerization was also evaluated. The increase of SPS concentration in feed was shown to decelerate the aniline polymerization (Fig. 4). This allows us to suppose a mechanism of the template synthesis of polyaniline in presence of the enzymes. On mixing the reacting compounds, some of aniline molecules react with SPS to form their complexes, whereas the other part remains in a free state. After the enzyme has been added, free aniline molecules are oxidized and their radical products produced during the enzymatic step migrate to SPS-aniline complexes. Therefore, these radicals initiate template polymerization of aniline to form PANI-SPS complex. We suggest that some radicals formed may react with free aniline molecules in bulk. However, the latter reaction is much less feasible, since the aniline concentration in its complex with SPS should be significantly higher than that in the volume. Even if some aniline molecules react in bulk, the formed oligomeric products immediately produce polyelectrolyte complexes with SPS. The proposed mechanism was confirmed by the UV-Vis spectroscopy detecting only the existence of polyaniline bound with SPS. Further alignment of polyaniline chain appears to be carried out due to the reaction of aniline oligomers stated in the complex with radical products formed by the enzyme.

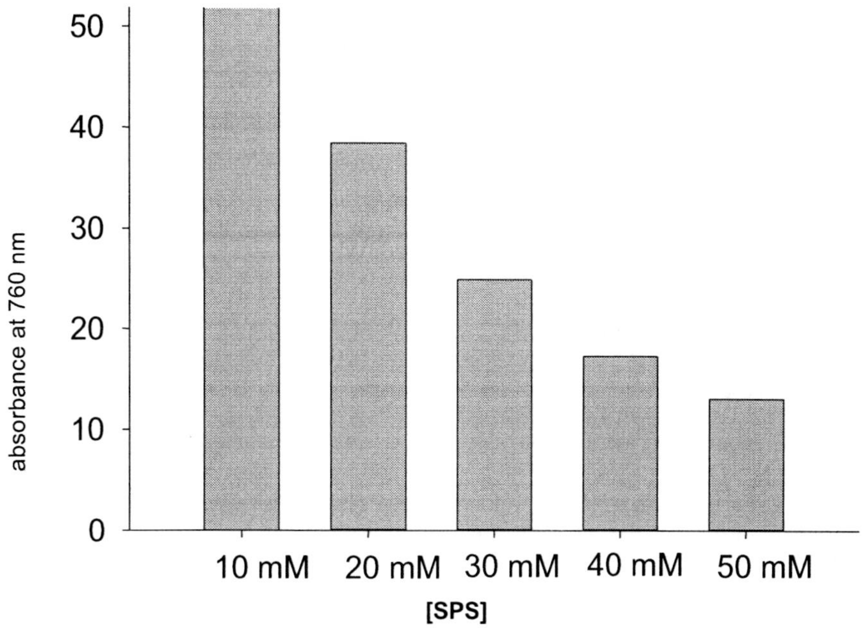

Figure 4. Effect of sulfonated polystyrene concentrations on the rate of enzymatic production of SPS-polyaniline complex.

Under favorable conditions, the aniline polymerization catalyzed by laccase proceeds for 4-5 days (Fig.5). So, at this time interval, the laccase does not lose its specific activity in the reaction medium. However, for the preparative production of PANI, it is necessary to conduct the reaction at a higher rate. For this, the concentration of dioxygen, in the reaction medium, should increase. Since dioxygen is gas, there are some technical problems to do this.

In the case of RPTP, the oxidant is hydrogen peroxide, a liquid, the concentration of which can be varied with no problems. Hydrogen peroxide concentration was shown to affect the rate of aniline polymerization. The initial rate of enzymatic polymerization increased with H_2O_2 concentration in feed up to 1.5 mM H_2O_2. (Fig.6A). These results well agree with the classical "ping-pong" mechanism of peroxidase catalysis (eqs. 1-3).

$$E + H_2O_2 \Rightarrow Cpd\ I + H_2O \qquad (1)$$

$$Cpd\ I + AH_2 \Rightarrow Cpd\ II + AH\bullet \qquad (2)$$

$$Cpd\ II + AH_2 \Rightarrow E + AH\bullet + H_2O, \qquad (3)$$

where E is the ferric enzyme (resting form); Cpd I and Cpd II are Compound I and Compound II, the oxidised intermediates of peroxidases; AH_2 and $AH\bullet$ are the electron donor substrate and the radical product of its one-electron oxidation, respectively.

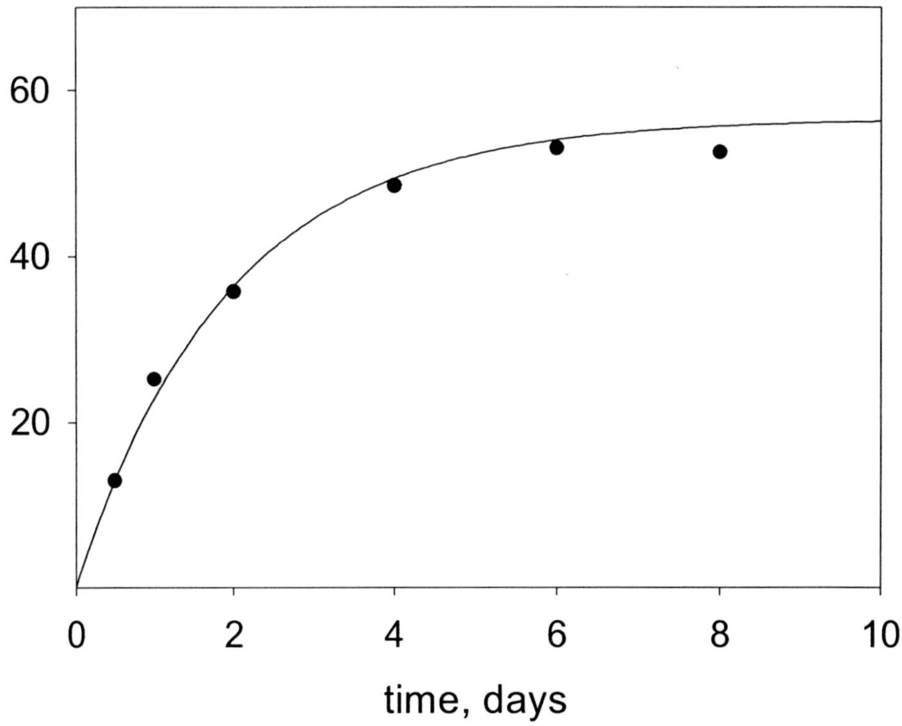

Figure 5. Kinetics of aniline polymerization in presence of sulfonated polystyrene catalyzed by laccase. Experimental conditions: 0.1 M citrate-phosphate buffer, pH 3.5; [aniline] = [SPS] = 50 mM; [laccase] = 5.5 x 10^{-7} M.

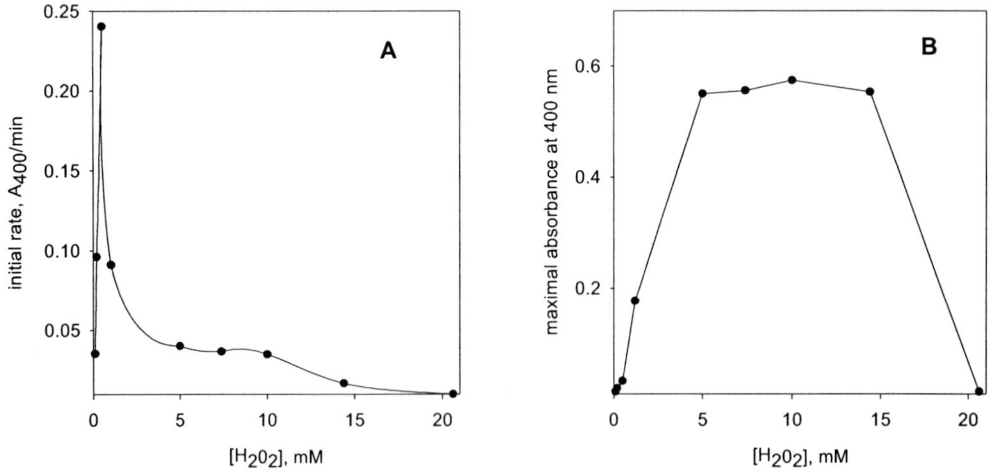

Figure 6. Effect of hydrogen peroxide concentration on the initial rate (A) and yield (B) of polyaniline template synthesis by royal palm tree peroxidase. Experimental conditions: 0.1 M citrate-phosphate buffer, pH 3.5; [aniline] = [SPS] = 100 mM; [RPTP] = 8.6 x 10^{-8} M. The maximal absorbance at 400 nm was recorded 3 days after the polymerization initiation.

However, at higher H_2O_2 concentration, the rate drops dramatically and at the concentration 20 mM, the aniline polymerization does not occur. Previously, the mechanism of inactivation of peroxidases by hydrogen peroxide was studied in detail [21, 22]. H_2O_2 concentrations higher than optimal result in some side reactions. A significant portion of Compound II could be oxidized by H_2O_2 to Compound III (eq. 4):

$$\text{Cpd II} + H_2O_2 \Rightarrow \text{Cpd III} + H_2O \quad (4)$$

Compound III is an active intermediate of peroxidase cycle. However, its activity is lower than that of Compound I and Compound II.

Compound I could also react with hydrogen peroxide producing the inactive form of the enzyme, verdohemoprotein (P-670):

$$\text{Cpd I} + H_2O_2 \Rightarrow (\text{Cpd I} \cdot H_2O) \Rightarrow \text{P-670} \quad (5)$$

Therefore, H_2O_2 is the suicide substrate for peroxidases. The optimal H_2O_2 concentration depends on peroxidase source and on the concentration of the second substrate (AH_2) present in feed [23].

Comparison of absorbance values, at 400 nm (this wavelength is characteristic for PANI [24]), of the reaction media, produced in presence of various H_2O_2 concentrations and measured after a complete termination of the reaction, showed that the yield of the aniline polymerization increased with H_2O_2 concentrations up to 5 mM (Fig. 6B). Further increase in H_2O_2 concentration did not increase the reaction yield. Furthermore, at 20 mM H_2O_2 the polymerization was not observed due to complete RPTP inactivation. Therefore, the most favorable conditions, for RPTP-catalyzed aniline polymerization, are 100 mM citrate-phosphate buffer (pH 3.5) containing 100 mM aniline, 100 mM SPS and 5 mM H_2O_2.

Calculations, based on the mechanism of peroxidase catalysis (eqs.1-3), showed that one H_2O_2 molecule needs two aniline molecules to be oxidized. So, for the whole pool of aniline molecules, contained in feed (100 mM), to be polymerized, H_2O_2 is to be added a few times adjusting the reagent concentration to or less than 5 mM. Earlier, some chemists indicated the necessity to conduct the peroxidase-catalyzed synthesis with periodical additions of H_2O_2 [8, 25, 26]. However, we found no publications where H_2O_2 concentration in feed was controlled during peroxidase-catalyzed synthesis of any compound.

Upon kinetic study of aniline polymerization monitoring the absorbance at 400 nm, we showed that at a single addition of hydrogen peroxide, the reaction was completed for 120 min. Addition of a new hydrogen peroxide portion up to 5 mM reinitiated the polymerization and the reaction proceeded again at the initial rate. Hence, all H_2O_2 molecules were consumed for 120 min under the reaction conditions.

Since, at a single H_2O_2 addition in feed, the chemical reaction is completed 120 min after its initiation, the preparative synthesis of PANI-SPS complex was carried out by adding new H_2O_2 portions every 2 h. The kinetics of synthesis of the complex is presented in Fig. 7. Contrary to the chemical radical polymerization normally used for PANI production, the enzymatic method allows one to kinetically control the process of aniline polymerization.

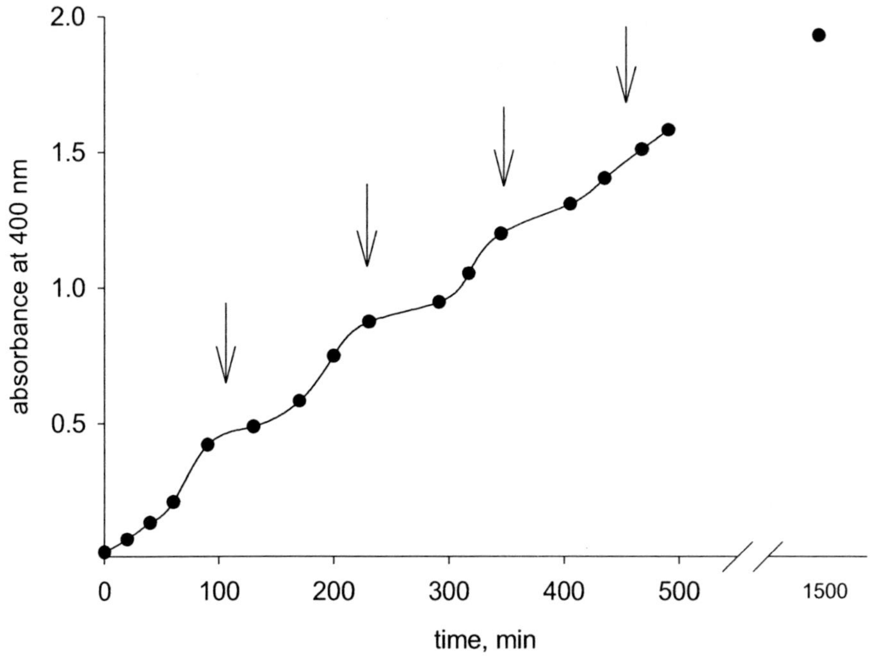

Figure 7. Kinetics of the preparative synthesis of polyaniline-sulfonated polystyrene complex catalyzed by royal palm tree peroxidase. Experimental conditions: 0.1 M citrate-phosphate buffer, pH 3.5; [aniline] = [SPS] = 100 mM; [RPTP] = 4.3 x 10^{-7} M. Hydrogen peroxide was added in feed every 120 min (see arrows) up to the concentration 5 mM. Absorbance at 400 nm was measured for PANI-SPS complex samples diluted by 41 using the reaction buffer.

Thus, using *C. hirsutus* laccase and the peroxidase isolated from royal palm tree leaves, stable and active under acidic conditions, we elaborated the enzymatic approach to production of the electroactive form of polyelectrolyte PANI-SPS complex. The advantage of this approach is that these enzymes catalyze the polymerization of aniline under environmentally friendly conditions.

Acknowledgment

The work was supported by NATO Science Programme (grant LST.CLG.978865) and the Russian Foundation of Basic Researches (grant 02-04-48885).

References

[1] MacDiamid AG. *Synthetic Metals* 2002, **125**, 11-22

[2] Anand J, Palaniappan S, and Sathyanarayana DN. *Prog. Polym.Sci.* 1998, **23**, 993-1018

[3] Pron A, and Rannou P. *Prog. Polym. Sci.* 2002, **27**, 135-190

[4] Tatsuma T, Ogawa T, Sato R, and Oyama N. *J.Electroanalyt.Chem.* 2001, **501**, 180-185

[5] Liao Y-H, Angelopoulos M, and Levon K. *J.Polym.Sci., Part A* 1995, **33**, 2725-2729
[6] Tzou K, and Gregory RV. *Synth.Met.* 1993, **55-57**, 983-988
[7] Roy BC, Gupta MD, Bhoumik L, and Ray JK. *Synth.Met.* 2002, **130**, 27-33
[8] Lui W, Kumar J, Tripathy S, Senecal KJ, and Samuelson L. *J. Amer. Chem. Soc.* 1999, **121**, 71-78
[9] Nagarajan R, Tripathy S, Kumar J, Bruno FF, and Samuelson L. *Macromolecules* 2000, 33, 9542-9547
[10] Pina DG, Shnyrova AV, Gavilanes F, Rodríguez A, Leal F, Roig MG, Sakharov IY, Zhadan GG, Villar E, and Shnyrov VL. *Eur. J. Biochem.* 2001, **268**, 120-126
[11] Chattopadhyay K, and Mazumdar S. *Biochemistry* 2000, **39**, 263-270
[12] Koroleva-Skorobogatko OV, Stepanova EV, Gavrilova VP, Morozova OV, Lubimova NV, Dzchafarova AN, Yaropolov AI, and Makower A. *Biotechnol. Appl. Biochem.* 1998, **28**, 47-54
[13] Sakharov IY, Castillo JA, Ariza JC, and Galaev IY. *Bioseparation* 2000, **9**, 125-132
[14] Sakharov IY, Vesga Blanco MK, Galaev IY, Sakharova IV, Pletjushkina OY. *Plant Sci.* 2001, **161**, 853-860
[15] Rodríguez A, Pina DG, Yélamos B, Zhadan GG, Castillo León JJ, Villar E, Gavilanes F, Roig MG, Sakharov IY, and Shnyrov VL. *Eur.J.Biochem.* 2002, **269**, 2584-2590
[16] Sakharov IY, and Sakharova IV. *Biochim. Biophys. acta*, 2002, **1598**, 115-121
[17] Karamyshev AV, Shleev SV, Koroleva OV, Yaropolov AI, and Sakharov IYu. *Enzyme Microb.Technol.* 2003, **33**, 556-564
[18] Sakharov IYu, Vorobiev Ach, and Castillo Leon JJ. *Enzyme Microb.Technol.* 2003, **33**, 661-667
[19] Su S-S, and Kuramoto N. *Synthetic Metals* 2000, **108** 121-126
[20] Rannou P, Gawlicka A, Berner D, Pron A, and Nechtschein M. *Macromolecules* 1998, **31**, 3007-3015
[21] Hiner ANP, Hernandez-Ruiz J, Rodriges-Lopez JN, Arnao MB, Varon R, Garcia-Canovas F, and Acosta M. *J.Biol.Inorg.Chem.* 2001, **6**, 504-516
[22] Rodriges-Lopez JN, Lowe DJ, Hernandez-Ruiz J, Hiner ANP, Garcia-Canovas F, and Thorneley RNF. *J. Amer. Chem. Soc.* 2001, 123, 11838-11847
[23] Arnao MB, Acosta M, del Rio JA, Varon R, and Garcia-Canovas F. *Biochim. biophys. acta* 1990, **1038**, 85-89
[24] Stejskal J, Kratochvil P, and Helmstedt M. *Langmuir* 1996, **12**, 3389-3392
[25] Uyama H, Maruichi N, Tonami H, and Kobayashi S. *Biomacromolecules* 2002, **3**, 187-193
[26] Mejias L, Reihmann MH, Sepulveda-Boza S, and Ritter H. *Macromol. Biosci.* 2002, **2**, 24-32

In: Biocatalytic Technology and Nanotechnology
Editor: G. E. Zaikov, pp. 105-117
ISBN 1-59454-117-5

Chapter 10

The Influence of Some Unnatural Amino Acids on the Growth of Cell Populations Having Different Natures

S. Varfolomeyev, E. Efremenko, P. Krupyanko and P. Vrjesch
The M.V.Lomonosov Moscow State University, Lenin's Hills, 1/11,
119992 Moscow, Russia e-mail: sdvarf@enzyme.chem.msu.ru

Abstract

The interest in the development of approaches to incorporation of synthetic amino acids into proteins was stimulated by the possibility to solve a number of fundamental and practical tasks. Addition of fluorine-containing analogues of amino acids as components of media was shown to inhibit the cell growth and to reduce the accumulated cell biomass. The inhibition effects of amino acid analogues correlated with their concentration in the nutrient media. Major regularities of influence of unnatural amino acids on the growth of various types of cells are discussed.

Key words: amino acid analogues, cell proliferation, inhibiting effect

Introduction

Theoretical and practical interest in "unnatural" compounds present in living biosystems is well known from numerous publications [1-6]. The information about the first enzymatic reaction discovered in the *Streptomyces cattleya* cells catalysing the conversion of fluoride ion and S-adenosylmethionine to 5'-fluoro-5'-deoxyfluoroadenosine was recently published and discussed very widely in the Internet since that was a discovery opening a new biotechnological era for preparation of organofluorine compounds [1].

The objective of this research was to study the effect of unnatural amino acid analogues on the growth of cell populations. The amino acid analogues are, on the one hand, inhibitors of cell growth that can have the influence on some key enzymes of cell metabolism, and, on the other hand, they can be included in the protein structures and to affect the cell growth thereby.

We had the following major questions to solve at the start of this investigation:

1. How do various amino acid analogues affect various cell populations at the period of active growth?
2. What phase of cell population growth is most influenced by amino acid analogues?
3. Does the inclusion of some unnatural amino acids into cell proteins exist?

To respond to these questions, different types of cells, namely prokaryotes (*Escherichia coli*), thermophilic archaebacteria (*Thermus flavus*), eukaryotes (*Saccharomyces cerevisae* yeast) and grafted tumors of Erlich's sarcoma were investigated.

All methods used in the experiments with microbial cells and grafted tumors were described previously [2, 5]. Several compounds being the synthetic analogues of natural amino acids were examined for their influence on the kinetics of growth of different cell populations. The following compounds were used in this work as amino acid analogues:

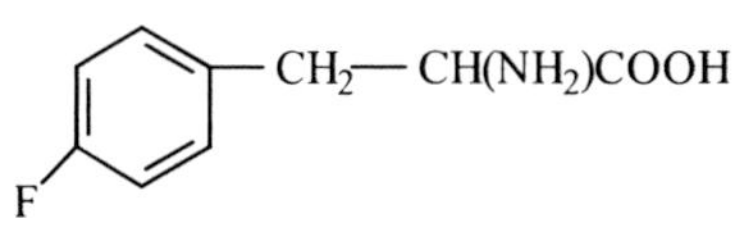

4-fluorophenilalanine, FPA (1)

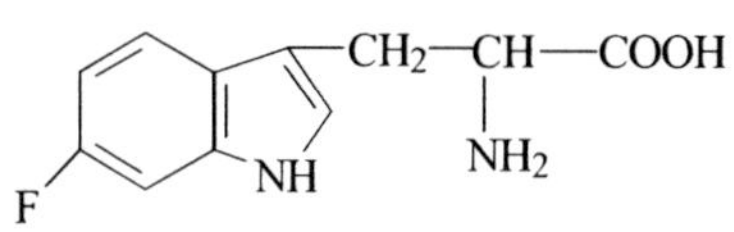

fluorotryptophane, FTrp (2)

$$HO-P(=O)(OH)-CH_2CH_2CH(NH_2)COOH$$

norleucine (3)

$$HO-P(=O)(OH)-CH_2CH(NH_2)COOH$$

2-amino-3-phosphonopropionic acid (4) (organophosphorus analog of aspartic acid)

$$HO-P(=O)(OH)-CH_2CH_2CH(NH_2)COOH$$

2-amino-4-phosphonobutyric acid (5) (organophosphorus analog of glutamic acid)

The Inhibition of E. Coli Cell Growth

The influence of compounds **1**, **3**, **4** and **5** on the growth kinetics of *E.coli* cells was investigated. All studied compounds appeared to be able to affect the growth of *E.coli* cells. However, the mechanisms of this influence differed. The typical curves for *E.coli* cell growth observed in presence of various concentrations of compound (**1**) are presented in Fig.1 The induction period during the first two-four hours of cell growth was revealed. Comparison of results showed that FPA does not practically affect the specific rate of cell growth at the exponential phase, but notably reduces the maximum yield of biomass accumulated up to the steady state phase.

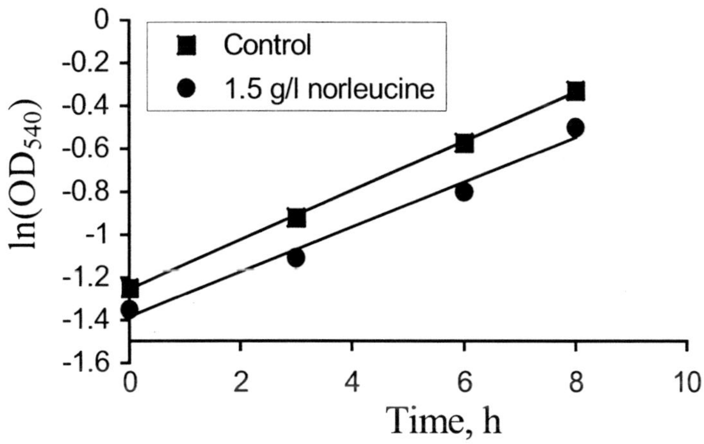

Fig.1. Growth of *E.coli* cells at various 4-fluorophenilalanine concentrations in the nutrient medium.

For comparison, the relative values of maximum biomass yield and the specific rate of growth of *E.coli* cells calculated from the exponential phase data are shown in Fig. 2. Obviously, compound **1** has a prevalent effect on the maximum yield of biomass. The mathematical processing of data revealed that $I_{c50,}$ calculated from two curves of Fig. 2. (μ and $\Delta D(21h)/\Delta D_o$), has different values, namely, 0.35 g/l and 0.9 g/l.

It was shown that the pattern, discovered for the action of norleucine on *E.coli* cell growth, was totally identical.

The growth kinetics of *E.coli* cells in the nutrition medium, supplemented with various concentrations of norleucine, was investigated (Fig.3). The results of the kinetic study of cell growth in the control pattern and the sample at maximum norleucine concentration (1.5 g/l) are presented in semilogarithmic coordinates in Fig. 4a.

The starting parts of both curves are actually parallel and can be characterized by the same specific rate of growth (μ_o=0.48±0.05 h^{-1}, $\mu_{(1.5\ g/l)}$ =0.42±0.05 h^{-1}). There is a big difference between the two curves in the middle of exponential phase of cell growth. The I_{c50}, calculated from the values of cell densities, accumulated in presence of various norleucine concentrations, was 1.7 g/l.

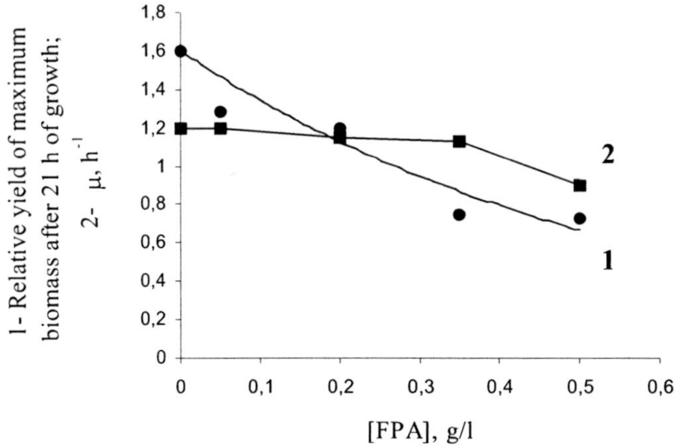

Fig.2. Relative yield of maximum biomass and specific rate of growth of *E.coli* cells vs. 4-fluorophenilalanine concentrations in the medium

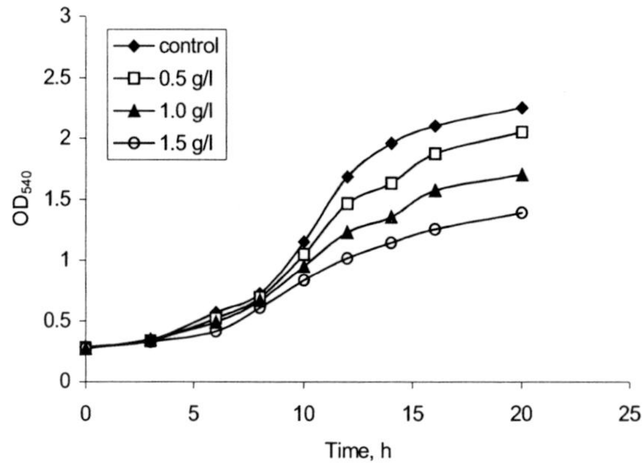

Fig.3. Growth of *E.coli* cells at various norleucine concentrations in the nutrient medium.

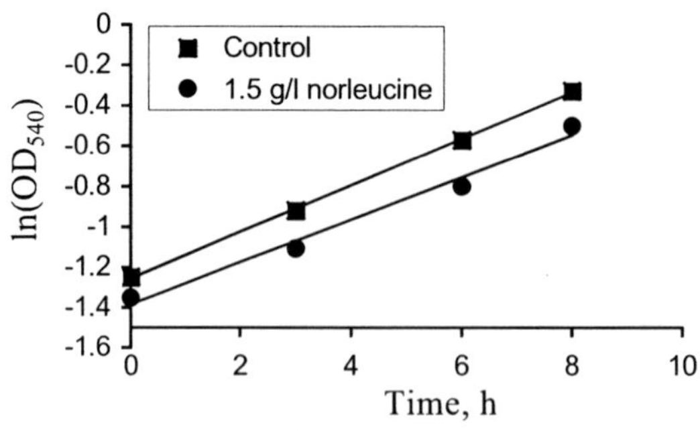

Fig.4. Linearization of initial parts of growth curves, obtained for *E.coli* cells in presence (1.5 g/l) and absence of norleucine, in semilogarithmic coordinates.

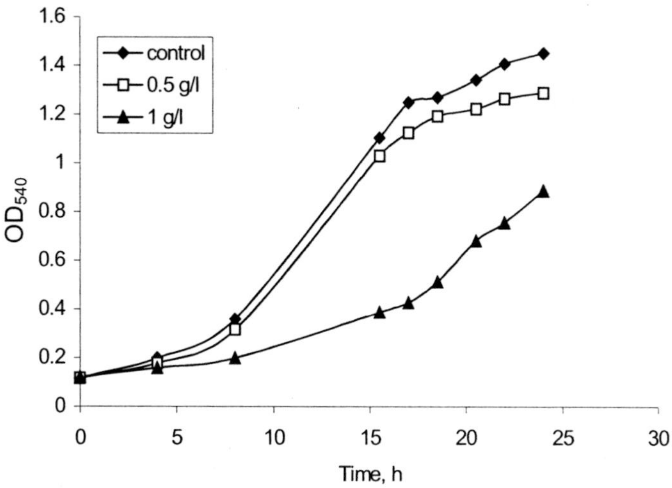

(a)

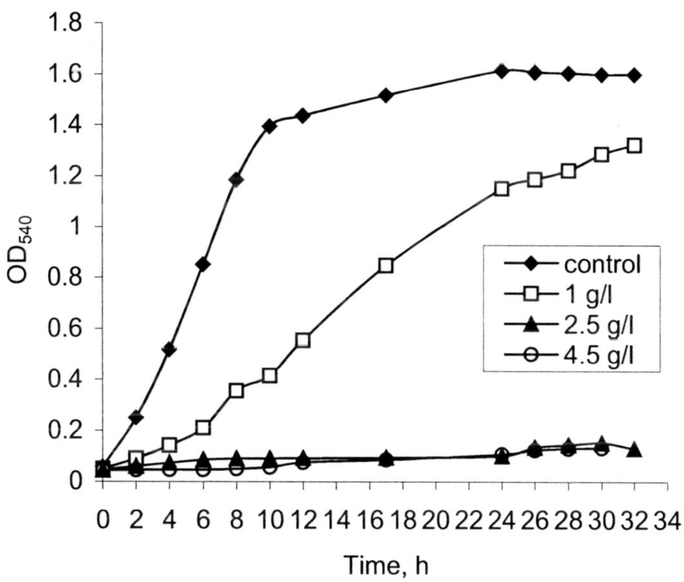

(b)

Fig.5. Growth of *E.coli* cells at various concentrations of 2-amino-3-phosphonopropionic acid (a) and 2-amino-4-phosphonobutyric acid (b) in the nutrient medium.

The organophosphorus analogues of aspartic and glutamic acids (compounds **4** and **5**) manifested entirely different mode of action on of *E.coli* cell growth. Their major influence was related to the reduction of specific rate of cell growth at the exponential phase.

The kinetic curves of cell growth in presence of organophosphorus analogues of aspartic acid and glutamic acid are given in Figs. 5a and 5b, respectively.

Analysis of these data led to a conclusion about the blocking effect of compounds **4** and **5** on the cell growth directly at the exponential phase. The dependence of specific growth rate on the inhibitor concentration in the cultural medium can be described by the following equation:

$$\mu = \frac{\mu_0}{1 + I/K_i}.$$

The inhibition constant (K_i, the quantitative analog of J_{c50}) of cell growth can be determined from the specific rate of cell growth as a function of the inhibitor concentration. Its values for compound **4** and **5** appeared to be 1.5 g/l and 1 g/l, respectively (Figs. 6a and 6b).

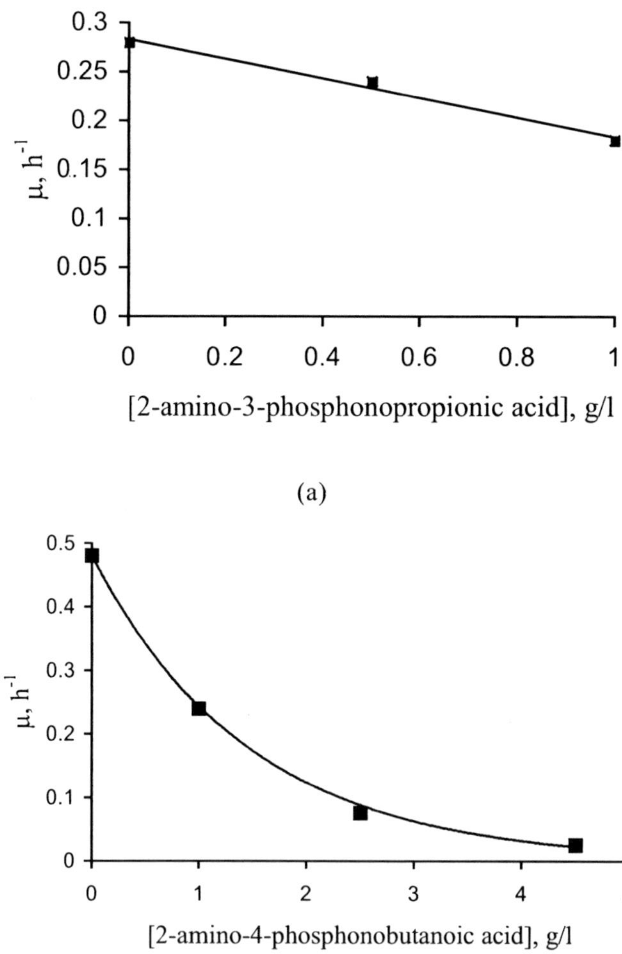

(a)

(b)

Fig.6. Specific rate of *E.coli* cell growth vs. concentrations of 2-amino-3-phosphonopropionic acid (a) and 2-amino-4-phosphonobutyric acid (b) in the nutrient medium.

THE INHIBITION OF THE ARCHEBACTERIUM THERMUS FLAVUS GROWTH

FPA inhibits the growth of *Thermus flavus* cells affecting the initial specific growth rate at the exponential phase (Fig. 7). The results characterize the dependence of relative values of maximum biomass yield, reached after cell cultivation for 15h, on FPA concentration are shown in Fig. 8. The inhibition constant value derived from the last figure is 0.8 g/l.

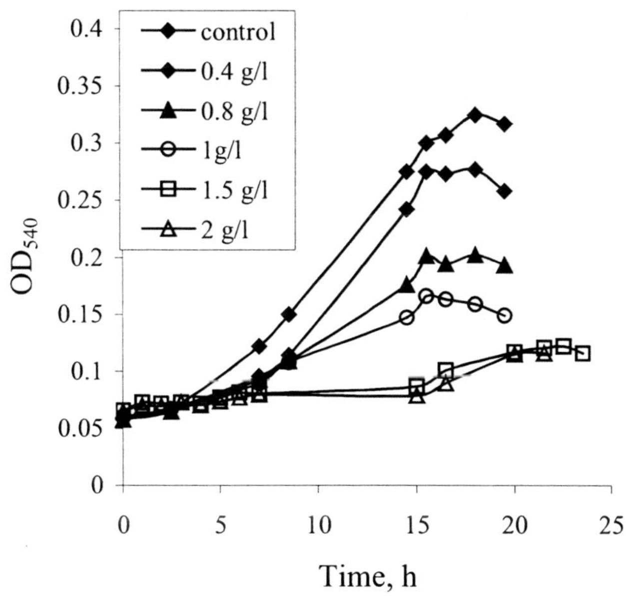

Fig.7. Growth of *Thermus flavus* cells at various 4-fluorophenilalanine concentrations in the nutrient medium.

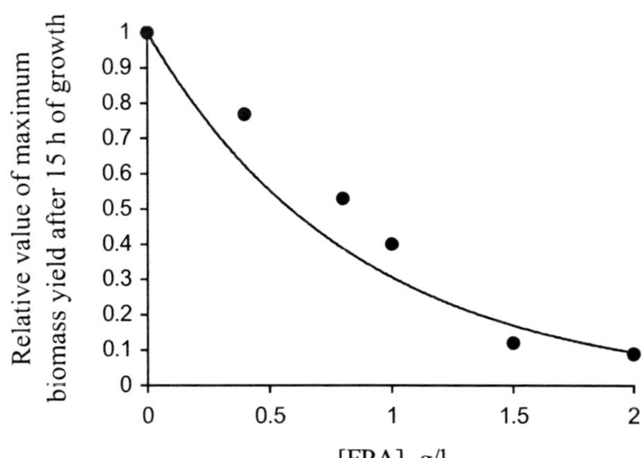

Fig.8. Relative yield of biomass and specific rate of *Thermus flavus* cell growth vs. 4-fluorophenilalanine concentrations in the medium

The effect of norleucine on the growth of thermophilic bacteria appeared to be quite complicated (Fig. 9). Norleucine added to the cultural medium showed a very weak effect on the cell growth for the first eight hours. Then the growth was notably inhibited after a weak activation. The inhibiting constant (J_{c50}) of norleucine, detected for the cells growing for 15 h in its presence, was 0.5 g/l (Fig. 10).

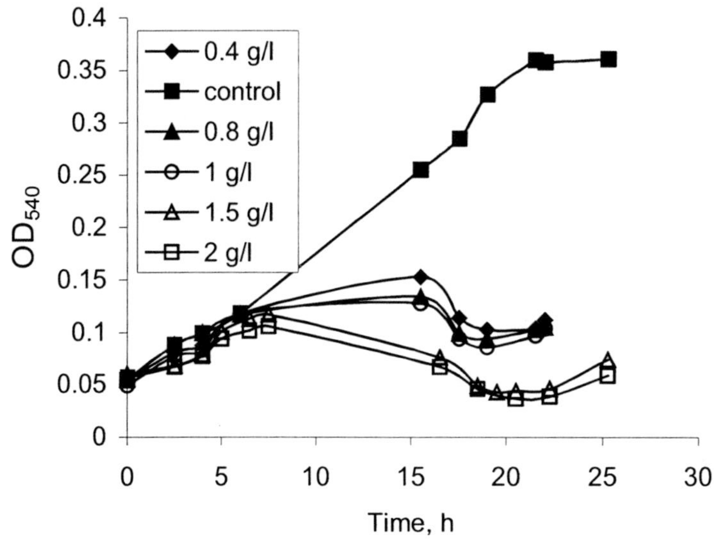

Fig.9. Growth of *Thermus flavus* cells at various norleucine concentrations in the nutrient medium.

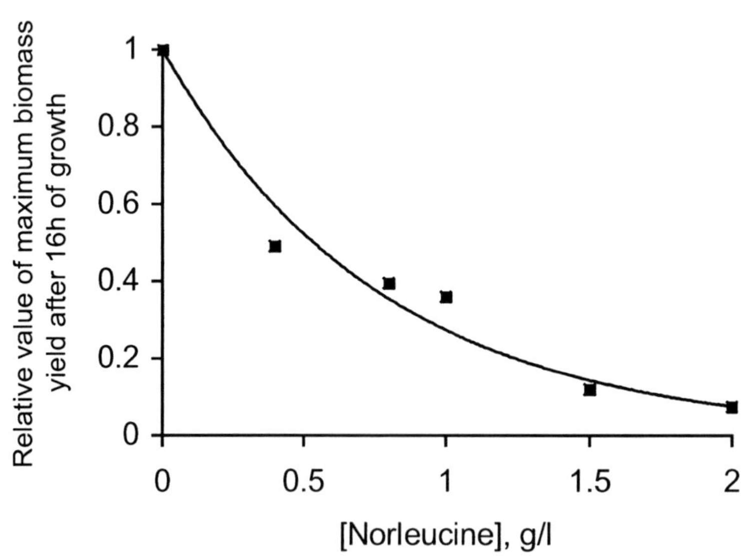

Fig.10. Relative yield of biomass and specific rate of growth of *Thermus flavus* cells vs. 4-fluorophenilalanine concentrations present in the medium

THE INHIBITION OF S. CEREVISAE CELL GROWTH

The yeast was revealed to be the most tolerant microorganisms to the unnatural analogues of amino acids inhibiting the cell growth. Actually, even high concentrations of analogues do not affect the cell growth. The results demonstrating the effect of norleucine on *S. cerevisae* cell growth are presented in Figs. 11 and 12. The last figure shows the inhibiting effect to increase up to some maximum level, and the further increase in norleucine concentration in the medium actually has low effect on the population growth. This phenomenon becomes more evident after application of FPA as amino acid analogue.

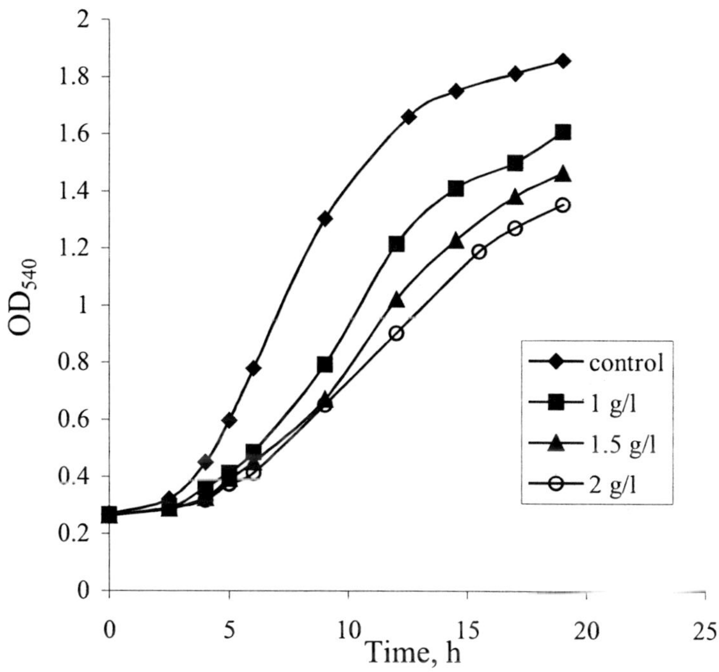

Fig.11. Growth of *Sacharomyces cerevisiae* cells, strain 232, at various norleucine concentrations in the nutrient medium.

Several yeast strains were used to investigate the kinetics of cell growth in the media containing various concentrations of FPA. The linearized data, obtained for the exponential phase of growth of yeast strain 232, are presented in Fig. 13. Similar lines were obtained for other strains studied. Figures 13 and 14 show that the influence of FPA on the yeast growth rates is rather complicated. It is possible to determine at least three concentration ranges of FPA influence on growth rates. There is no effect on the growth rates at FPA concentrations less than 0.1 g/l in the medium. The increase in FPA concentration up to 1 g/l reduces 1.5-fold the growth rate. At higher concentrations, the growth rate is independent of FPA concentration.

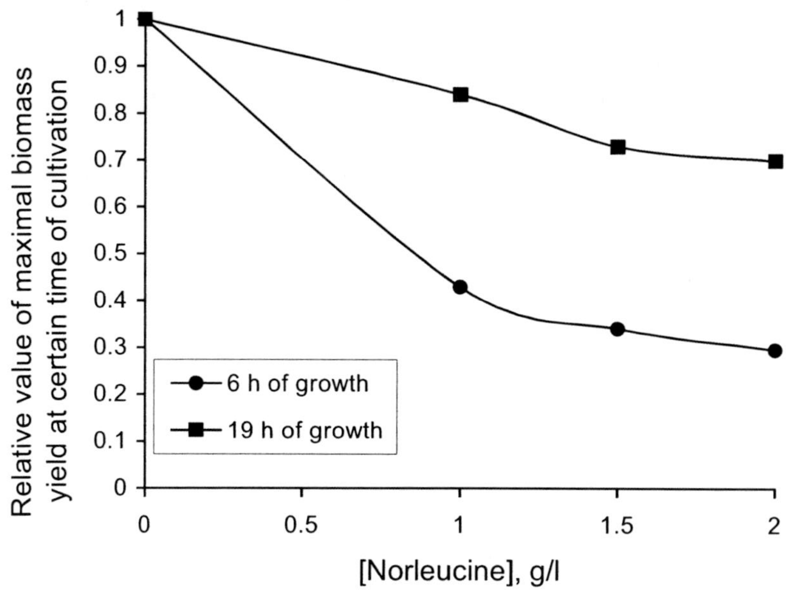

Fig.12. Relative yield of biomass and specific rate of growth of *Sacharomyces cerevisiae* strain 232 cells vs. norleucine concentrations in the medium

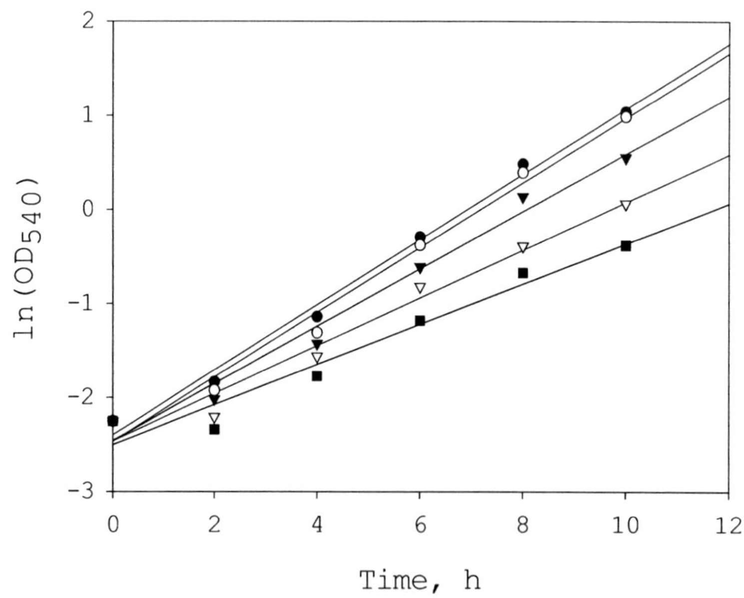

Fig.13.The growth of the *Saccaromyces cerevisae cells,* strain 232, at various concentrations of 4-fluorophenilalanine in the medium (mM): ● – 0, ○ – 0.27, ▼ – 0.55, ∇ – 2.73, ■– 5.46.

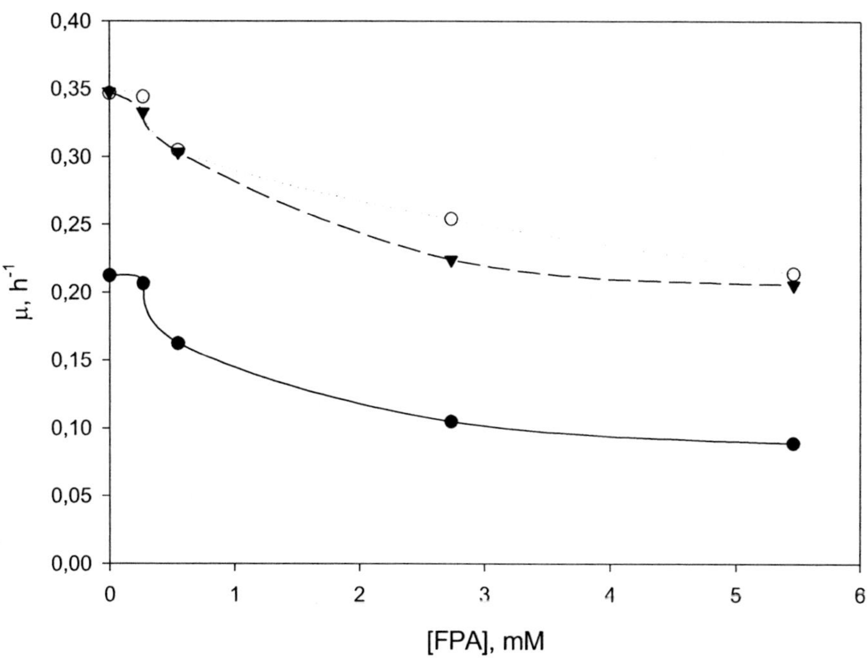

Fig.14. The growth rates (□) of various *Saccaromyces cerevisae* strains as a function of 4-fluorophenilalanine concentration (Strains numbers: ● – 230, ○ – 232, ▼– 233).

THE INFLUENCE OF FPA, FLUOROTRYPTOPHANE (FTRP) AND NORLEUCINE ON ERLICH'S SARCOMA GROWTH

The influence of FPA and norleucine on the growth of grafted tumor of Erlich's sarcoma was investigated. The tumor growth in 5 mice was estimated by gravimetric analysis. The data were averaged. The final results are presented in Fig. 15. The moments of intraperitoneal injection of analogues are marked with arrows. The single doses of FPA, FTrp and norleucine injections were 1.7 mg/mouse, 1.2 mg/mouse and 1.1 mg/mouse, respectively.

The growth of tumor in absence of injections of amino acid analogues was used as control. The tumor growth, in the control sample, was revealed to be exponential. The dynamics of tumor growth changed considerably in presence of analogues. The weight of tumor increased up to some constant level and the rate of growth became zero. It is clear that three investigated compounds showed the cytostatic effect.

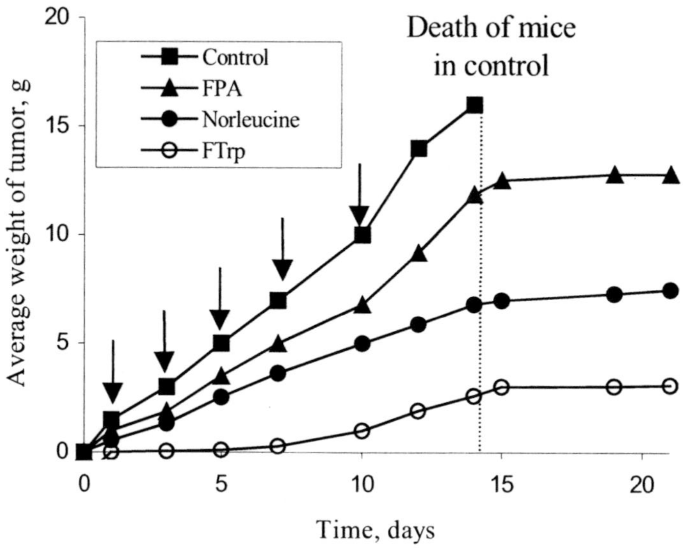

Fig.15. Kinetics of tumor growth (Erlich's sarcoma) grafted to mice without (control) and with injections of 4-fluorophenylalanine, fluorotryptophane and norleucine.

THE SUBSTITUTION OF NATURAL PHENYLALANINE (PHE) BY FPA IN THE TOTAL PROTEIN CONTENT OF S.CEREVISAE CELLS

The above results show *S. cerevisae* cells as being the living organism most resistant to the inhibiting effects of FPA and norleucine. So, the yeast cells were taken as test object to study the possibility of FPA incorporation into the proteins of living organisms.

The *S.cerevisae* cells were cultivated in the liquid medium with 1 g/l FPA. Results of amino acid analysis showed a significant part (35-40 %) of Phe to be replacable by FPA. The same FPA/Phe ratio was obtained with cells growing in the medium containing 5 g/l FPA.

The investigation illustrates a possibility of development of living systems with a significant part of natural amino acids replaced by their organoelemental analogues.

The substitution of certain natural amino acids by their analogues in the microbial proteins can result in development of new biotechnological processes, based on application of new microbial strains, or in interruption of synthesis of key enzymes of cell metabolism modifying their protein structures. The introduction of amino acid analogues and their derivatives into the proteins of cells, characterized by high proliferating rates, can afford the development of new anticancer and biocide preparations.

REFERENCES

[1] D. O'hagan, C.Schaffrath, S.L. Cobb, J.T. G. Hamilton, C.D. Murphy: *Nature*, 416, 279 (2002)

[2] A.E. Pojitkov, E.N. Efremenko, S.D. Varfolomeyev: *J.Mol.Catal.* B:Enzymatic, 10, 47 (2000).

[3] R. Larson, S. Dhar, H. Ehrsson, P. Nygren, R. Lewensohn: *Br.J.Cancer,* 78, 328 (1998).

[4] J. Parsons, G. Xiao, G.Gilliland, R.Armstrong: *Biochemistry*, 37, 6286 (1998).

[5] S.D. Varfolomeyev, E.N. Efremenko, V.V. Verkhusha, P.V. Vrzheshch: *Vestnik Mosk.Universit.* (in Russian), 41 (6), 352 (2000).

[6] A.K.Johri, M.Yalpani, D.L.Kaplan: *Biochem.Eng.J.,* 16 (2), 175 (2003).

In: Biocatalytic Technology and Nanotechnology
Editor: G. E. Zaikov, pp. 119-126
ISBN 1-59454-117-5

Chapter 11

THE SIGNIFICANCE OF PROTEINASE-INHIBITORY BALANCE IN TEARS FOR THE STUDY OF PATHOGENESIS AND ELABORATION OF METHODS FOR THERAPY AND PROGNOSIS OF A BURN WOUND HEALING IN THE EYE

N. B. Chesnokova[a], T. P. Kuznetsova[a], N. F. Kazanskaya[b], O. A. Kost[b], I. I. Nikolskaya[b], O. V. Beznos[a], T. A. Pavlenko[a], E. P. Stoliarova[a] and O. E. Skirgello[b]

[a]The Helmholtz Moscow Research Institute for Eye Diseases, Sadovaya-Chernogriazskaya 14/19, 103064 Moscow, Russia; Fax: 7-(095) 923-4161
[b]Chemical Enzymology Department, Chemistry Faculty, The Lomonosov Moscow State University, 119992 Moscow, Russia
E-mail: kost@enzyme.chem.msu.ru; Fax: 7-(095) 939-5417

ABSTRACT

The proteinase-inhibitor balance in rabbit lacrimal fluid and the clinical course of the disease were comparatively studied at various periods after alkali eye burn of various locations. The balance was shown to depend on the stage and character of the wound healing process, as well as on location of the burn. The regulation pathways of the level of proteinases and inhibitors in the eye after the burn were demonstrated.

Key words: eye burn, wound healing, proteinase-inhibitor balance, proteolytic enzymes, angiotensin-converting enzyme

The eye has a unique structure representing all kinds of tissues and metabolic processes running in the organism. For this reason, the study of the eye can be of interest both to ophthalmologists and to the general medicine specialists as well as to researchers of various fields of biology. In 1969, Stewart Duke Elder called the eye "...a complete biochemical laboratory which is rapidly becoming fascinating not only to the ophthalmologist who wishes to know the fundamental metabolism of the organ which he has made his speciality, but also to the general physiologist and biochemist who will find here everything in miniature" [1].

The eye traumas (military, industrial, criminal and domestic) are now getting on one of the first places as a cause of blindness and poor vision. Their therapy is a complicated medical problem and needs further study of the injury process and search for new efficient therapeutic methods. The trauma model of the anterior eye segment in rabbits is a very convenient object for examination of both eye wounds and general mechanisms of the injury process. Due to the cornea transparency it is possible to estimate quite precisely the dimensions of the epithelial injury, the depth and area of stromal ulceration, corneal neovascularization and the edema degree. Likewise, the merit of the model is the possibility to examine the tear fluid film on the anterior eye surface where the developing metabolic processes reflect those running in the eye. The tear fluid is taken from the alive animal by the non-invasive method and allows one to estimate the dynamics of the parameters under study in the same creature.

The injury healing process dynamics depends on interaction of various metabolic systems and is controlled by various bioregulation pathways. Proteolytic enzymes play an important role in reparation [2, 3]. Proteinases participate in elimination of necrotic tissues from the wound through nonspecific proteolysis of damaged protein molecules. Upon their excessive uncontrolled activation, the native tissues can be proteolytically lysed enlarging the wound. Insufficient activities of these enzymes disorder the reparative process course, namely, slow the wound healing and lead to the rough scar formation. However, the role of proteolysis is much wider than a mere nonspecific proteolysis of structural proteins. There is a limited proteolysis resulting in cleavage of one or a few bonds in a protein molecule, which leads to formation of many biologically active compounds. The limited proteolysis is one of regulation pathways providing a rapid physiological response of the organism to various affects. Proteolytic reactions take part in the protein synthesis, activation, inactivation and modification of various enzymes, the formation of regulatory peptides, cytokines and the factors of immune system, blood clotting, fibrinolysis, etc. The reactions of limited proteolysis play an important role in regulation of the wound process in all stages since they provide the interaction between various metabolic systems as well as the interaction between the tissue processes and hemovascular regulation.

Tissue injury entails the inflow of various proteolytic enzymes into the wound from cells and intracellular structures, from the vascular bed and from the inflammatory infiltrate cells. The spacing between proteinases and their substrates – structural and functional proteins – is deranged because of disruption of cells, the increased permeability of blood vessels, cellular and intracellular membranes. The control over proteolysis starts mainly by numerous inhibitors of proteolytic enzymes, and the endogenous inhibitors do not always suffice to sustain the hyperactivation of proteolytic processes.

After the traumatic injury of the anterior segment of the eye, proteolytic enzymes are secreted by various sources to tear fluid. The proteolytic enzymes come to the injury area from the damaged cells. Dilatation of conjunctival vessels and increase in their permeability leads to the ingress of plasma enzymes into the tear fluid. In a few minutes after the corneal damage, polymorphonuclear leukocytes were observed to accumulate in limbic vessels from where they migrate into the peripheral area of cornea and into the tear fluid [4]. In addition to polymorphonuclear leukocytes, the sources for proteolytic enzymes in tears are various cells of uninjured area of conjunctiva – mucosa covering the anterior eye surface and the inner surface of eyelids, which intensely reacts to the traumatic process. The inhibitors of proteolytic enzymes can flow through the microcirculatory bed and can be synthesized locally.

As a response to trauma, the inflammatory reaction starts. Its intensity and pattern depend on the features of both the injuring affect and the reactivity of the organism. However, the stages of inflammatory-reparative processes and their sequence are similar. The clinical course of reparative processes after the trauma notably depends on balanced interaction between proteolytic enzymes and their inhibitors. Our preliminary studies of the state of proteinase-inhibitory balance in cornea and in tear fluid showed that one can judge about the condition of the proteinase-inhibitory balance in the injured cornea from the activities of proteinases and their inhibitors in tear fluid [5].

The purpose of our research is to study the activities of some proteolytic enzymes and some of their inhibitors in tear fluid of rabbits at various periods of the burn wound healing in the anterior eye segment and to search for the efficient ways of correction of proteinase-inhibitory balance.

We modeled the standard severe alkali burns of equal area and depth in rabbit eyes. For corneal burn and for the combined corneal and conjunctival burn, we used the circular fine cotton tissue pieces ∅=7 mm soaked with 10% NaOH to place it on the relevant eye area for 40 sec. For the restricted limbal burn, a strip of the same tissue (2 mm wide) was placed on the eye surface along all the limbus. After the removal of the tissue, each eye was washed with 20 ml of physiological solution. For anesthesia, 5% ketamine (1 ml/kg) was subcutaneously injected. Local epibulbar anesthesia was conducted by instillation of 0,5% dicaine.

Tear fluid was collected from animals before the burn and on the 1, 3, 7, 14, 21 and 28 days after the burn. Circular pieces of filter paper were placed into the conjunctival fornix for 5 min. Tear components were then eluted by physiological solution. The eluate was centrifuged and the supernatant examined.

The activity of trypsin-like serine proteinases, α_2-macroglobulin proteinase inhibitor and the antitrypsin activity (ATA) were determined by the modified spectrophotometric method using N-benzoyl-D,L-arginine-p-nitroanilide (BAPNA) as substrate [6]. The total activity of cysteine proteinases [7] and the activities of tissue and plasma kallikreins were measured using N-carbobenzoxy-L-phenylalanyl-L-arginine-7-amino-4-metylcoumarin (Z-Phe-Arg-MCA) as substrate in presence of group-specific inhibitors [8]. The activity of angiotensin-converting enzyme was measured fluorometrically using the synthetic substrate N-carbobenzoxy-L-phenylalanyl-L-histidyl-L-leucine (Cbz-Phe-His-Leu) [9]. Total protein level in the eluate was estimated by the Lowry method [10].

The clinical course of the eye burn healing in rabbits was followed on the 7, 14, 21 and 28 days after the burn biomicroscopically without staining and with 0,5% fluorescein staining of the anterior eye surface. Fluorescein stains cornea lacking the epithelium and allows one to estimate the epithelial defect area. The degrees of clinical manifestations of the wound process were expressed in conventional units. The state of perilimbal vessels of conjunctiva, corneal edema, corneal neovascularization, area and depth of corneal ulceration were estimated.

After the corneal burn, the epithelial defect visually disappeared mostly on the 3rd day, reappeared on the 7th day and was followed by stromal ulceration. Without treatment, the deepest corneal ulcers appear by the 3rd week after the burn and the scar forms by the 28th day.

Activities of all enzymes and inhibitors under study depended on the wound process stage and on its clinical course character. Despite various properties and functions of the tested proteinases, which we will not discuss now, all enzymes turned out to have a few peaks of a notable activity increase relevant to the stages of the wound healing process (Fig. 1). The proteinase activity peaks coincided with the periods of increased corneal ulceration on the 3rd-7th and 14th-21st days. Along with the enhanced activity of proteinases, the activity of their inhibitors decreased. This is explicable by their binding to the enzymes, proteolytic cleavage and by the action of free oxygen radicals on their active sites [11]. The significance of the proteinase-inhibitory disbalance, for development of corneal ulceration after the burn, was attested by the discovered difference in the ratio of proteinases to antiproteinases upon favorable (ulceration of the upper and middle cornea layers) and unfavorable (ulceration of deep layers up to corneal perforation) clinical course (Fig. 2). In the favorable process, the mean proteolytic enzyme activity was lower than in the unfavorable one. Conversely, the mean concentration of inhibitors was lower in the unfavorable course.

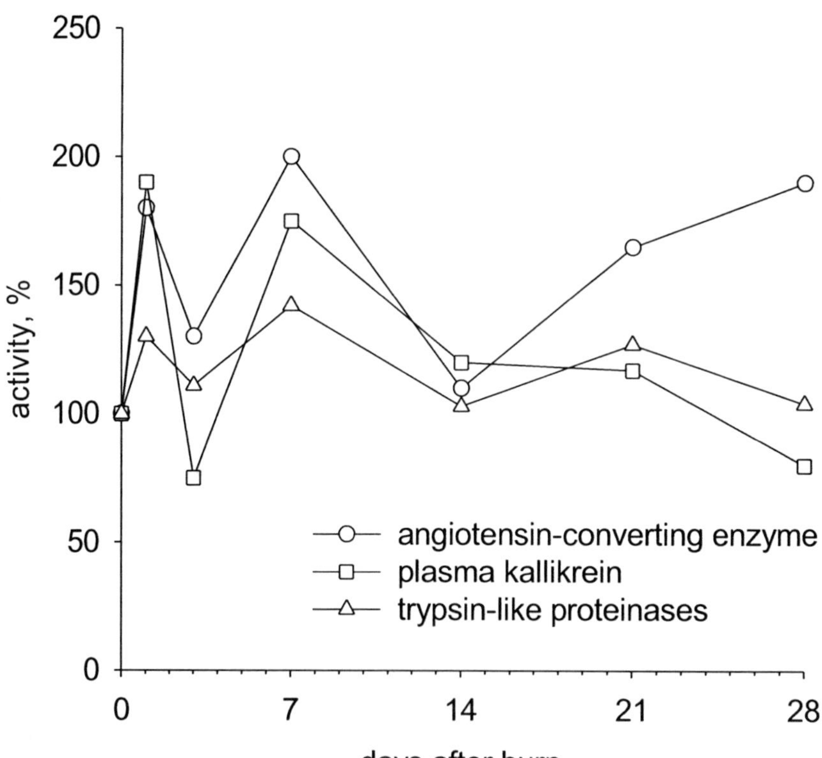

Fig.1. Dynamics of the activity of proteolytic enzymes in the tear fluid of rabbits after the severe alkali burn of cornea.

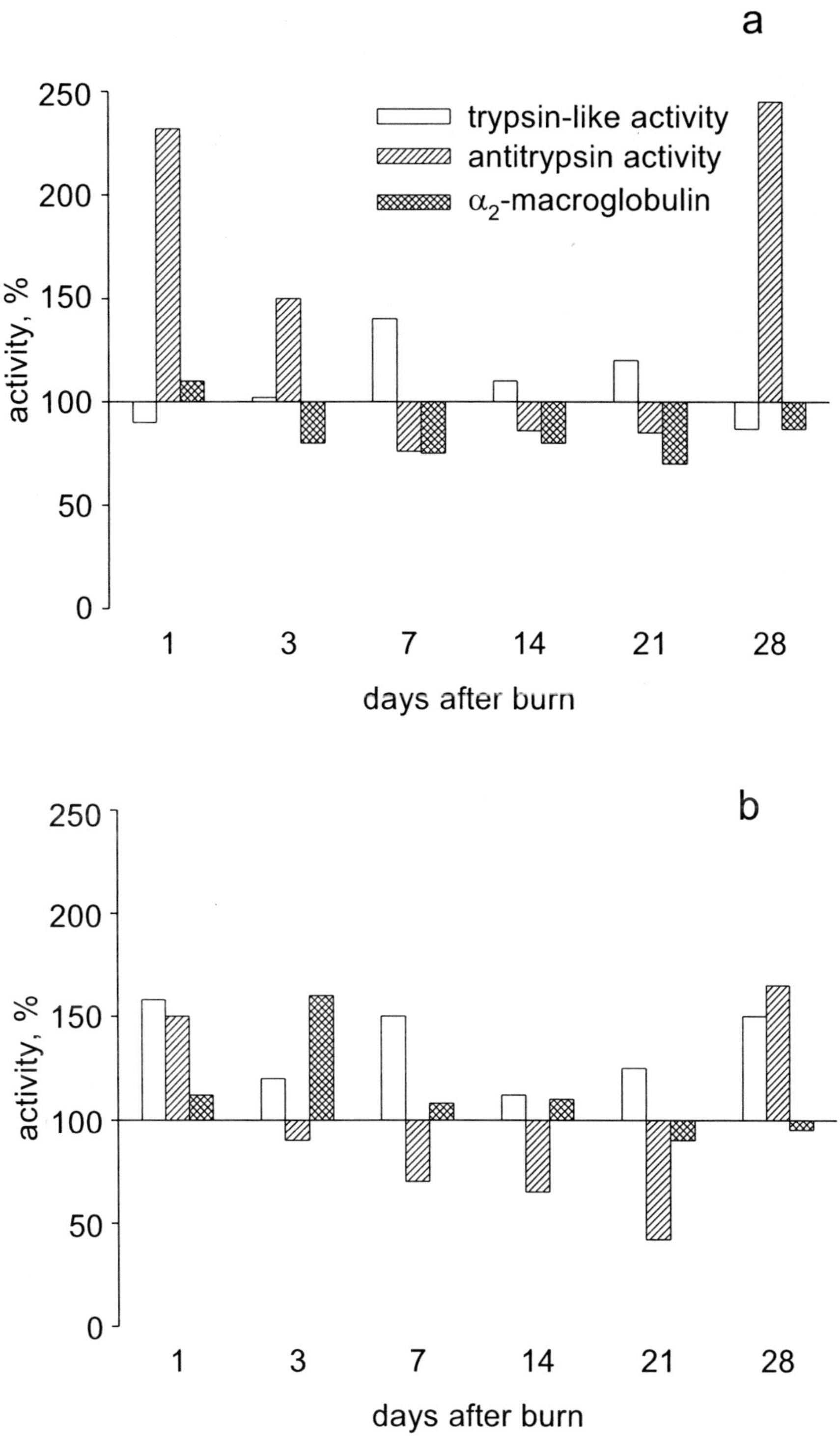

Fig.2. Dynamics of the trypsin-like activity, antitrypsin activity and α_2-macroglobulin level in the tear fluid of rabbits after the severe alkali burn of cornea (the activity of these parameters in intact rabbits is taken to be 100%): a) favorable clinical course of the wound healing; b) poor healing.

In eye burn traumas, there is usually a combined injury of cornea, conjunctiva and limbal area. The effects of burn location on the character of the clinical course of the healing process and on the tear fluid composition still needs further investigation. We tried to compare the clinical course of the experimental eye burn healing and the changes of some parameters of the proteinase-inhibitory balance in tears, after the following eye injuries, equal in area and depth: a) corneal only; b) the combined injury of cornea, conjunctiva and limbus; c) the total burn of the limbal area [12]. The latter case was interesting because the limbal zone is known to be a source of the stem cells for the corneal epithelium [13].

The healing process after the combined partial burn of cornea, adjacent conjunctiva and limbal fragment was established to run easier and with fewer complications than after the burn of the central part of cornea equal in depth and area. Changes in the activity ratio of proteolytic enzymes to their basic inhibitors were adequate in this case, which provided the rapid and complete reparation. The total burn of limbal area was the most severe eye trauma, accompanied by the most pronounced shifts in the proteinase-inhibitory balance in tear fluid; it caused deep organic changes both in cornea and inner eye structures leading finally to their subatrophy.

Thus, the results of our research showed that the activities of proteolytic enzymes and their inhibitors in tear fluid depend on the stage of the wound healing process, on the burn location and on the clinical course of the healing process. Estimating the proteinase-inhibitory balance state in tear fluid one can prognosticate the outcome of the healing process, define the ways of its correction and evaluate the efficiency of therapy. Our results show the necessity of application of antiproteolytic preparations. With this aid, we applied the instillations of aprotinin – the inhibitor of serine proteinases (Fig. 3), and instillations of ovomucoid – the inhibitor of serine and cysteine proteinases. The effect of antiproteolytic preparations consisted in a lower frequency of deep corneal ulcers, a lower manifestation of inflammation and the formation of a more tender scar [14, 15]. Application of antiproteolytic preparations was efficient if the instillations were made no longer than within 14 days after trauma; their further application decelerated the reparative processes.

The proteolytic enzymes are known to be applied to clear the wounds from necrotic tissues that improve the reparative processes [16]. We supposed that applying the proteolytic enzyme for the first two days after the trauma and then the antiproteolytic preparation for the following 12 days could increase the therapeutic efficacy. The proposed method for correction of proteolytic processes permitted us to reduce the inflammatory reaction, to stimulate the reparative regeneration of corneal epithelium and stroma and to prevent the deep corneal ulceration [17]. In this case the activity of endogenous proteinases in tears was lower whereas that of inhibitors higher than in untreated rabbits.

The data of various authors show that traumas, especially burns, are often accompanied by a pronounced immune suppression and by a disturbed regulatory effect of immune system on reparative processes. We studied the effect of the immune system stimulation on the clinical pattern of the corneal burn healing in rabbits and on the proteinase-inhibitory balance in tear and blood [18]. For this purpose, rabbits were immunized by the complete Freund's adjuvant before the alkali burn of the cornea. It is noteworthy that immunization shifted the proteinase-inhibitory balance in tear fluid toward the inhibitory activity growth whereas no similar changes in blood were observed. This was possibly related to the influence of the conjunctival immunocompetent cells. In the group of immunized rabbits, the new blood vessels grew faster into the wound area and the corneal ulcers were less severe. In these animals the local protective-adaptive reaction of proteolytic enzymes and their inhibitors in tear fluid developed faster. We observed a similar reaction of proteinases and their inhibitors in tear fluid after the treatment of eyes injured with a gas flow containing the high concentration of nitrogen oxide (NO) [19]. One of the mechanisms of NO action is the acceleration and enhancement macrophage reaction after the trauma, which was histologically confirmed in our experiments.

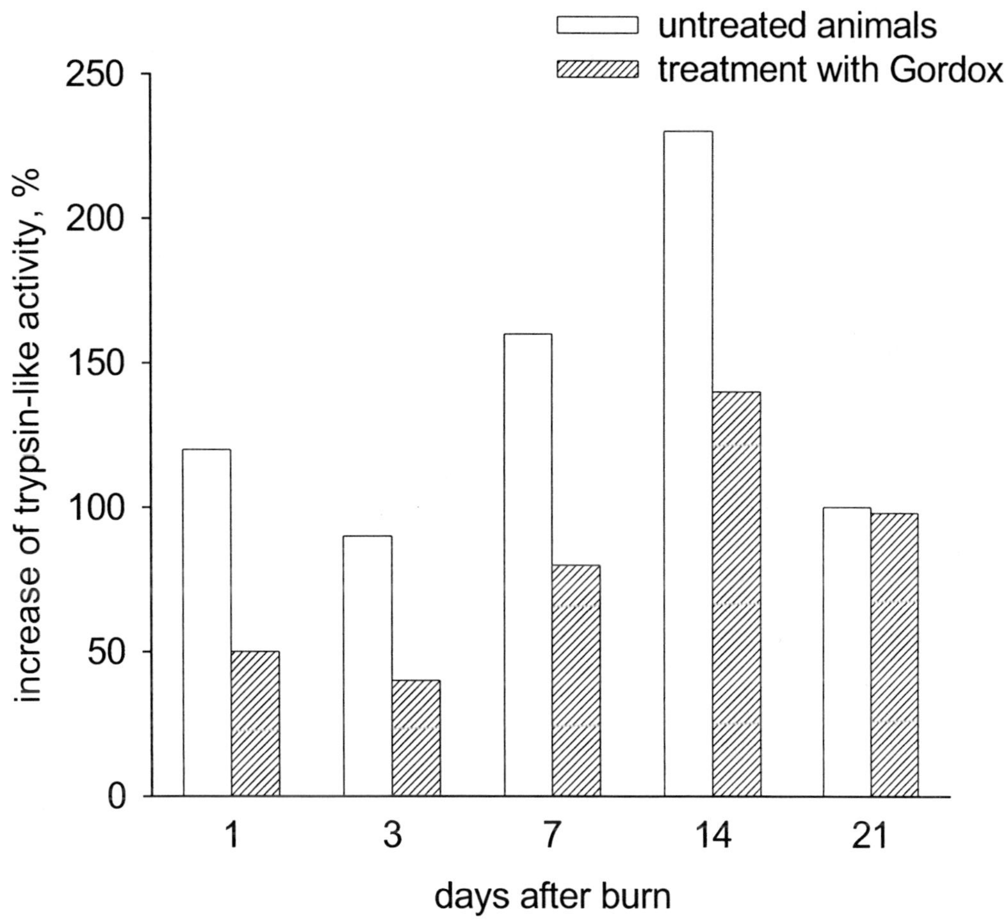

Fig. 3. Influence of treatment with antiproteinase (Gordox, active component – aprotinin) on the increase of trypsin-like activity in the tear fluid of rabbits after the severe alkali burn of cornea.

Thus, the study of the proteinase-inhibitory balance in tear fluid after the eye trauma is promising for both the study of metabolic processes during the corneal wound healing and the elaboration of new efficient ways of therapy.

ACKNOWLEDGEMENTS

This work was supported by the Russian Foundation for Basic Research, grants 02-04-48700, 03-04-06003.

References

[1] C.N. Greymore: *Biochemistry of the eye*. Academpress, London & New York, 1970. 783 p.

[2] L.A. Lokshina: *Usp. Biol. Chim.*, 18, 162 (1977).

[3] L.A. Lokshina, N.I. Solovyova, V.N. Orekhovich: *Vopr. Med. Chim.*, 5, 38 (1987).

[4] J. Burnett, L. Smith, J. Prause et al.: *Invest. Ophthalmol. Vis. Sci., Arvo Suppl.*, 20, 173 (1981).

[5] N.B. Chesnokova, G.G. Bordiugova, S. Bagdash et al.: *Oftalmol. Zh.*, 1, 52 (1987).

[6] A.A. Pokrovsky: *Biochemical methods in clinic*. Meditsina, Moscow, 1969, 652 p. (in Russian).

[7] E. A. Dilakyan, N.I. Solovyeva, L.Z. Topol: *Vopr. Med. Chim.*, 6, 36 (1991).

[8] T.P. Kuznetsova, N.B. Chesnokova, T.S. Paskhina: *Vopr. Med. Khim.*, 4, 79 (1991).

[9] O.A. Kost, N.B. Chesnokova, T.P. Kuznetsova: *Vopr. Med. Khim.*, 42 (2), 130 (1996).

[10] O. Lowry, N. Rozebrough, A. Farr et al.: *J. Biol. Chem.*, 193, 265 (1951).

[11] D. Johnson, J. Travis: *J. Biol. Chem.* 254, 4022 (1979).

[12] N.B. Chesnokova, P.V. Makarov, O.V. Beznos: *Vestn. Oftalmol.*, 2, 38 (2001).

[13] F.E. Kruse: *Eye*, 8 (2), 170 (1994).

[14] R.A. Gundorova, G.G. Bordugova, I.P. Choroshilova et al.: *Klin. Mbl. Augenheilk*, 197, 1 (1990).

[15] E.V.Egorova, R.A.Gundorova, G.G.Bordugova et al.: *Klin. Mbl. Augenheilk,* 198, 28 (1991).

[16] V.N. Strutchkov, A.V. Grygoryan, V.K. Gostyshev et al. (Eds): *Proteolytic enzymes in purulent surgery*. Meditsina, Moscow, 1970, 408 p. (in Russian).

[17] Y.A. Kapitonov, E.V. Chentsova, N.B. Chesnokova et al.: *Vestn. Oftalmol.,* 112 (5), 11 (1996).

[18] O.V. Gulidova, O.V. Beznos, S.Z. Shatinina, N.B. Chesnokova: *Vestn. Oftalmol.,* 3, 35 (2002).

[19] N.B. Chesnokova, R.A. Gundorova, O.I. Kvasha et al.: *Vestn. Ross. Akad. Med. Nauk*, 5, 40 (2003).

In: Biocatalytic Technology and Nanotechnology
Editor: G. E. Zaikov, pp. 127-141
ISBN 1-59454-117-5

Chapter 12

BIOCATALYTIC TECHNOLOGIES FOR CHEMICAL SYNTHESIS, ENVIRONMENTAL PROTECTION, ANALYTICAL SYSTEMS AND MEDICINE

E. Zaitseva
Faculty of Chemistry, The M.V. Lomonosov Moscow State University, Vorobiovy Gory 1/11, 119992 Moscow, Russia, Fax: (095)-939-54-17
E-mail: zai@enz.chem.msu.ru

ABSTRACT

The review covers recent progress in the research works developed in the framework of the project «Biocatalytic Technologies» of the Federal targeted scientific-technological program «Research and methodology in the priority trends of development in science and technology".

The new elaborated biocatalysts-based technologies for industrial application and agriculture are described. Based on enzymes, the high-sensitivity methods and devices for medical and ecological purposes as well as for control of food quality, industrial production and environmental monitoring are characterized. The examples of drugs and materials being studied for therapy of cardiovascular and oncological diseases, for surgery and ophthalmology, based on enzymes and their regulators, are presented.

Key words: biocatalysis; biocatalytic technologies; enzymes, enzymatic preparations; ecotoxicants; biosensors; bioanalytical test-systems; bioluminescence; drugs based on enzymes and their regulators; wound dressing; enzyme inhibitors; microencapsulation; eye injury healing

Biocatalysis is one of the most attractive fields for investments in biotechnology. The world market of biocatalysts, including enzymes, substrates and the devices based on them, is estimated at several billions USD and permanently keeps growing. The enzymatic preparations are widely applied in various industrial fields (textile, pulp-and-paper, chemical, food, pharmaceutical), agriculture (fodder additives, veterinary preparations), medical and ecological diagnostics as well as drugs.

The application scale of enzymes and enzyme-based catalysts depend on the ever-growing contribution of biocatalytic technologies to the economy of developed countries. The scientific trends, in the coming decades in Russia, will retain the topicality of the following researches and applications of biocatalysts:

1. Biocatalytic technologies for industrial and agricultural purposes;
2. Biocatalysts for fine organic synthesis;
3. Biocatalysts for environmental protection;
4. Biocatalytic systems for medical and ecological diagnostics;

Sensor technologies;

5. Drugs based on enzymes and their protein regulators;
6. Biocatalysts in the systems of production and application of renewable sources of energy and ecologically pure fuels.

This paper reviews the new results of research and developments obtained by scientists in the Lomonosov Moscow State University and some other research institutes from Russian Academy of Sciences, performed in the above trends in the framework of the project "Biocatalytic technologies" of the Federal targeted scientific – technological program "Research and methodology in the priority trends of development of science and technology".

1. Enzymes and Biocatalysts for Industrial and Agricultural Purposes

The most notable works in this trend are those resulted in creation of high-efficiency biocatalysts with new improved properties for bioconversion of vegetal matter and cellulose wastes, for treatment of fabric articles, for production of fodder additives, for chemical synthesis, pharmacology and veterinary. Such developments are the preparations based on carbohydrates (cellulases, hemicellulases, pectinases amylases, xylanases, mannanases), oxidoreductases (laccases, peroxidases), cyclodextrine transferases, formate dehydrogenases, etc.

The Lomonosov Moscow State University, Institute for Biochemistry and Physiology of Microorganisms (Russian Academy of Sciences) and All-Russian Research Institute of Applied Biotechnology in collaboration with other research institutions from Russian Academy of Sciences and affiliated research institutes as well as private companies (OOO "FermTech", OOO "PromFerment" etc.) have conducted some research and developments aimed at production of industrial enzymatic preparations of cellulases, β-glucanases, xylanases, mannases, galactanases, arabinases, pectinases, xyloglucanases, α- and β-galactosidases, α-amylases and glucoamylases for their applications as fodder additives for agricultural animals and poultry as well as in production of beer and alcohol, in textile industry, in detergents production, in pulp-and-paper industry, etc. [1-11]. Much attention was given to low-scale laboratory research methods, adequately mimicking the processes of enzyme application in industrial scale. As enzyme producers, the microbial strains

Trichoderma, Penicillium, Aspergillus and Bacillus were used with their productivities notably increased by mutagenesis and selection as well as via optimization of cultivation processes. Similarly, the extracellular enzymatic complexes, produced by wild and mutant strains of the above mentioned microorganisms, were studied for their composition and properties. Individual enzymes were isolated for the complexes playing a key role in applications of enzymatic preparations in various industrial and agricultural fields. The fermentation plant (the town Berdsk), producing biological preparations and other enzyme-producing plants in Russia successfully produce liquid and dry forms of enzymatic preparations.

In the Bach Institute of Biochemistry, the application of cellulases, hemicellulases and xylanases for creation of ecologically safe processes for cellulose bleaching and the mild methods for defibring various kinds of paper upon its production is studied. At present, the industrial processes include the enzymatic processing for the waste paper difficult for defibring into cellulose mass by use of the preparation "Cellokandin" derived from *Geotrichum candidum* [12]. The second subject under study is a possibility of application of the enzymes derived from the mutant strain *Geotrichum candidum* 3C-106 with various ratios of cellulases and xylanases for intensification of bleaching the sulphate softwood and hardwood unbleached cellulose [13,14]. The third research subject is the comparative study of laccases from various basidial fungi as well as the laccase-mediator systems promising for application in biotechnological processes for degradation of ecotoxicants, for bleaching the paper pulp, for deriving chemical compounds from lignin, for producing bioplastics, biofuel cells, etc. The most productive strain of *Trametes (Coriolus)* fungus was selected and the promising medium chosen that is appropriate for industrial production of cultural fluid with a high oxidase activity. A new class of efficient laccase mediators (1-phenyl – 3-methyl – pyrazolones) was disclosed [15-17]. Parameters of intermediates, formed upon enzymatic oxidation of these compounds, were studied. HPLC was used to conduct the quantitative assay of conversion of lignin model compound, veraltyl alcohol, in laccase-mediator system. The results were compared to identical data obtained for 2,2'-azinobis-(3-ethylbenzthiazoline-6-sulfonate) (ABTS), a widely applied laccase mediator.

Enzymes are unique catalysts for enantioselective synthesis of organic compounds. For the late two decades, a large number of such processes were elaborated and put to practice where the enzymes of various classes – oxidoreductases, hydrolases, transferases, etc. were involved. In Moscow State University, the works are performed on creation of recombinant formate dehydrogenases with predetermined properties for regeneration of NAD(P)H coenzymes practically important for industrial production of chiral and physiologically active compounds [18-22]. The methods of site-specific mutagenesis on the basis of data on three-dimensional structure of formate dehydrogenase from *Pseudomonas* sp. 101 bacteria were used to obtain the enzymatic preparations of formate dehydrogenases with altered properties, showing the higher activity, thermal and chemical stabilities. The procedures have been elaborated to obtain a unique, having no natural analogs enzyme with the changed coenzymatic specificity from NAD^+ to $NADP^+$ as well as the enzyme with a wide pH optimum (6.0–9.0) of activity. For the both biocatalysts, the processes were created for their large-scale production using recombinant *E.coli* strains, which reduces the cost by a factor compared to the conventional process of deriving formate dehydrogenase from *Candida boidinii* yeast.

Of importance is the application of enzymatic processes in production of beta-lactamic antibiotics. New research developments and approaches elaborated at the Belozersky Institute for physical-chemical biology helped to optimize the reactions of enzymatic synthesis of new penicillins and cephalosporins in concentrated aqueous solutions, in heterogeneous systems "water solution – precipitate", in oversaturated water solutions and upon conduction of solid-phase enzymatic reactions [23-26]. The enzymatic synthesis was shown to become notably more efficient due to a well-directed choice of reaction conditions and its control, reached for late years, on the basis of knowledge of the mechanism and kinetics of enzymatic reactions of acyl transfer [27,28].

To develop the processes for industrial synthesis of cyclodextrines providing the demands of the internal market in Russia, the scientists at Kazan State University develop the biocatalysts based on cyclodextrine transferases, synthesizing mostly β-cyclodextrine, and derive promising isolates belonging to the bacteria of *Pceudomonaceae* and *Bacillaceae* families [29,30]. The research resulted in the development of recombinant microbial strains and cell cultures of plants, hyperproducers of cyclodextrine transferases as well as in their immobilized forms. It helped to create a laboratory collection of producers of cyclodextrine transferases isolated from Tatarstan soils.

The research works conducted in the framework of the project "Biocatalytic technologies" aim at creation of new ecologically pure energy sources, biofuel cells, having some advantages compared to conventional fuel cells. They function in mild environmental conditions and are constructed on the basis of renewable materials. The present-day hydrogen fuel cells, directly converting hydrogen energy into electricity, have a Platinum catalyst as a constituent part, which makes them very expensive; their electrode is very sensitive to carbon oxide (CO) and hydrogen sulfide (H_2S) admixtures, contained in industrial hydrogen. To-date, the experimental devices have been designed and constructed for enzymatic fuel electrodes based on hydrogenase, not inferior to Platinum ones [85-87].

2. Biocatalytic Systems for Environmental Protection, Ecological and Medical Diagnostics

Degradation of ecotoxicants resulting from industrial activities as well as bioremediation of contaminated natural and technogenic media usually supposes the application of biocatalytic methods. In recent years, the researches of Moscow State University created some efficient ecobiotechnologies by use of biocatalysts based on microorganisms as well as studied their possible applications on real environmental objects.

So, the noteworthy preparation "Rhoder", was elaborated jointly with the All-Russian Institute of Petroleum and Gas for bioremediation of oil-contaminated soils and water surfaces [31-33]. The preparation consists of two bacterial species *Rhodococcus rubber* and *Rhodococcus erythropolis* showing a synergetic effect on oxidation of hydrocarbons. The results of the field trials, conducted in Western Siberia, the Arctic and Komi Republic areas, showed a high efficiency of "Rhoder" applications in open aquatic reservoirs and moderately contaminated (less than 20g/L) marshy swamps. The parameters of the biological activity of soil, after "Rhoder"applications, were within the highest values among other comparable technologies for biorecultivation of the oil-contaminated marshy swamps

The biocatalytic technologies for purification of waste water appear quite promising. New approaches have been designed to expand the applicability of high-speed anaerobic treatment of waste water at low temperatures (4-10°C), which is especially topical in the countries with cold climate. The results are successfully applied in the acting systems, including the anaerobic reactor with the upflow through a granulated biomass, for high-efficiency purification of liquid dungy run-offs as well as to increase the production of fertilizers and biogas and to reutilize water [34,35].

Of great promise are the developments of systems for decomposition of azo dyes, showing toxic, mutagenic and carcinogenic effects, by use of a mutagenic consortion of microorganisms [36,37]. By the example of the azo dye "Sirius" yellow, the efficiency of the new elaborated hybrid anaerobic–aerobic reactor was demonstrated for mineralization of azo dye-containing waste water resistant against biodegradation. The research showed a possibility to degrade three acid azo dyes (Acid Orange 6, Acid Orange 7, Acid Orange 52) by use of the biocatalyst based on granulated sludge from the aerobic EGSB reactor (the brewery "Efes-Moskva") [38].

A technological process almost without the use of reagents has been elaborated for hydrogen sulfide elimination and for elementary sulfur recuperation from contaminated gases and waste water [39-41]. The bioreactor contains *Thiobacillus* genus bacteria which can oxidize H_2S to elementary sulfur and transport it to an extracellular medium. The resulting sulfur is removed from the reactor by sedimentation and can become a marketable product (e.g. to manufacture sulfuric acid).

Of great practical importance for detection and destruction of highly toxic chemicals become the enzymatic preparations based on organophosphate hydrolase (OPH) capable of catalyzing the hydrolysis of some organophosphorus neurotoxins representing pesticides and chemical warfare agents [42]. New genetic constructions (pTES-His-OPH, pTrcTE-OPH) and strains were created to provide the high level of expression of OPH in a soluble form including that containing the oligo histidine sequence [43,44]. The derived samples show a higher catalytic activity in respect to some enzymatic substrates, an elevated temperature of their activity optimum and the pH optimum shifted to alkaline area compared to the native OPH. The methods of enzyme immobilization on fabric carriers were elaborated and the efficiency of developments application demonstrated as individual means for personnel protection as well as for detoxication of instruments and equipment surfaces.

An important trend in elaboration of new express-methods of analysis and diagnosis, highly sensitive and selective, is the creation of biosensor devices. The enzyme-based biosensors are leading nowadays among both the research developments and commercial sensor systems. Recent research results demonstrated the efficiency of new approaches to immobilization of enzymes as well as a notable increase in sensitivity and selectivity of the present-day amperometric biosensors via replacement of Platinum and peroxidase electrodes by those modified with Prussian Blue [45-47]. The sensor systems were created to analyse glucose, glutamate, ethanol, and lactate by use of a new portable express-assay. For biosensors, including hydrolytic enzymes, a transducer with the highest pH sensitivity was elaborated via modification of electrodes by polyaniline.

Successful research has been conducted on creation of biosensor systems for assaying inhibitors of cholinesterases presenting highly toxic pesticides [48-54]. A unique biosensor system was elaborated for analysis of neurotoxic esterase directly in the whole human blood enabling one to make early prognosis of symptomatic development of poisoning by organophosphorus compounds (OPC) [49-53]. Based on the flow-injector amperometric system for measuring the level of hydrogen peroxide, the automated biosensor analyzer was elaborated to assay some OPC and carbamates in samples of water, soil and foods [54].

A potent impact to development of new efficient technologies for creation of biosensors is the application of nanotechnological approaches and methods providing the information of biomolecule structure in nanometer range [55-60]. A new concept of bioassay is under way from counting the marker nanoparticles with the use of the atomic force microscopy to calculate single nanoparticles formed through biocatalytic polymerization of some substrates. An important element of the offered analysis is two new steps: measurements are made for both the overall intensity of analytic response and its spatial distribution; the useful signal is singled out by the image recognition technology [61]. The potentials of the offered approach were demonstrated by the example of the immunochemical assay of transferrin and virus particles.

To control the environmental contamination level and to detect toxins, the enzyme immunoassays are widely applied where the specificity is provided due to the interaction between antibodies and the detectable antigens. The required sensitivity is reached by use of various systems for assay of activity of enzymatic labels. At present, Russian researchers elaborated some enzyme immunoassay procedures for quantitative and qualitative control of the level of pesticide contamination of natural objects and foodstuffs, a greater number of which are certified and put to practice. A range of assayable compounds includes 2,4-dichlorophenoxyacetic (2,4-D), and 2,4,5-trichlorophenoxyacetic (2,4,5-T) acids [62-65], atrazine [66,67], simazine [68-70], chlorsulfuron [71-73] and their main destruction products. The sensitivity limit for various pesticides varies in the range 0.1–5 ng/ml at the assay time 10–60 min.

Successful research is conducted on creation of enzyme immunoassay test-systems with spectrophotometric and chemoluminescent detection of signal to assay antibiotics in foods. The experimental devices were elaborated to assay streptomycin and chloramphenicol (levomycetin) with detection limits 10 ng/ml and 0.03 ng/ml, respectively; the assay time is 30 min [73-75].

Another array of elaborated methods permit the group-specific immunological detection of non-ionic surfactants with a high sensitivity (10 ng/ml) to control the contamination of various water samples upon ecological monitoring and control of technological processes. It was established that the analysis in its operation range reveals not less than 85% surfactant molecules contained in the probe irrespective of the structural heterogeneity of preparations [76-78].

Express-detection of microorganisms, including the pathogenic ones is one of the most topical problems of the present-day diagnostics. Application of enzymes, capable of producing a quantum of light through chemical reaction, affords determination of microbial contamination degree of any object. These enzymes include firefly luciferase catalyzing D-luciferin oxidation in ATP presence, the universal intracellular metabolite. Luminescence of the reaction mixture is a factor used to measure the ultra-low quantities of ATP (up to 10^{-15}M) and the concentration of viable microbial cells (up to 10^3 cells/ml). This underlies the ATPmetry method of "fast microbiology" notably simplifying and several ten-fold shortening the procedure. The time of the bioluminescent assay is 6–10 h depending on the test sample instead of 24–72 h compared to conventional tests.

Researchers of Moscow State University elaborated the kits of bioluminescent reagents including the high-sensitivity ATP reagent based on recombinant firefly luciferase, ATP standard and the reagents for pretreatment of food samples under assay [79-83]. The kits are used to control microbial contaminations in various foods, such as milk, ice cream, whole and minced meat and water. A notable advance in practical application of the method was reached upon application of special cuvettes, filtravettes, manufactured from bacterial membrane filter, which permits one to completely eliminate the nonmicrobial ATP as well as to concentrate the microbial cells on the membrane filter [84]. This simplified the procedure of bioluminescent assay of microbial contaminations and brought the detection limit up to 200 cells in a luminometer cuvette. At present, the elaborated procedures are applied to assay the overall microbial contamination of raw milk (the detection limit 10^3 CFU/ml, the assay time 20 min.), raw minced meat (the detection limit 10^3 CFU/g, the assay time ~30 min.) and tap water (the detection limit 10^3 CFU/ml, the assay time 20 min. and the detection limit 1 CFU/ml, the assay time 6 h.; where CFU is the colony forming unit).

3. Drugs of New Generation, Based on Enzymes and Their Regulators

To-date, multiple research works on elaboration of drugs, based on enzymes and enzymatic systems, have been performed in Russia. Further endeavor in this field will soon lead to curative preparations for efficient and aftereffects-free thrombolysis, the effective and safe antioxidant compositions, the medicinals for therapy of injuries, infected wounds, bedsores and burns, including eye burns, for normalizing the proteolytic balance in the organism (cancer, digestive tract diseases, ischemias, etc.) and the antimicrobial medicines. Most preparations under way need to be chemically pretreated to reduce the organism immunogenicity, to increase the drug stability, to decelerate their clearance rate from the organism, to impart the capacity to interact at the cellular level. The above tasks are reached by various methods of conjugation, microencapsulation and immobilization of proteins and their specific modifications.

These developments can be exemplified by the results of researchers from the Institute for Experimental Cardiology and the Lomonosov Moscow State University. Thus, based on the conjugates of superoxide dismutase and catalase with chondroitin sulfate, the effective thrombolytic medicines were derived to protect the vascular walls [88]. Research on thrombolytic effect of native urokinase and its derivatives resulted in the optimal composition of urokinase–acyl–enzyme system providing its efficient persistence in the organism [89-91]. The enzyme "Longolytin" and other plasminogen activators were comparatively studied for their activating and fibrinolytic properties [92-94]. The application of this available and cheap medicament in Russia was shown to be effective to heal thromboembolic diseases. The active-site acylated derivatives of urokinase and enzyme "Longolytin" with prolonged thrombolytic effect were derived. Likewise, the study of the composition of acyl-urokinase and recombinant staphylokinase seems promising [95,96]. The complex study of the combined effect of pro-urokinase and staphylokinase enabled to reveal the synergy in their activities, which makes possible to reduce 3-4-fold the total therapeutic dose and the level of therapeutic side effects.

An original procedure was elaborated to produce soluble monomer fibrin by treatment of fibrinogen with the thrombin-like enzyme from the venom of *Agkistrodon halys* snake inhabiting on Russian territory. The derived monomer fibrin was used to elaborate a high-sensitivity kinetic method for assay of the cellular plasminogen activator [97].

Other successful works under way aim at producing the angiotensin-converting enzyme (ACE) inhibitors presenting a class of medicinals of the first choice and applicable to regulate the blood pressure. The general mechanism of functioning of two active sites in ACE has been studied and the inhibitor nature was shown to play a principal role in the efficiency of suppressing ACE activity [98,99]. Peptidomimetics were synthesized having the functional groups important for binding in ACE active site and showing the inhibitory activity. The experiments on animals demonstrated the efficiency of the synthesized inhibitors in therapy of alkaline and thermal burns of the eyeball [100].

To heal the diseases related to distortion in the organism proteolytic balance, the objective of the relative research under way is to create the medicinals based on inhibitors of plant and animal proteinases. They resulted in the following developments:

- the derived samples of peroral preparations, based on the Bowman-Birk soybean proteinase inhibitor (BBI), showing the antitumor and anticancer effects [101,102];
- the elaborated technology for production of aprotinin ("Inhiprolum" preparation) from bovine lungs [103-106];
- the derived unique systems for delivery of proteinase inhibitors in the form of prolonged polymer conjugates, microparticles, polymer micelles and biosoluble drug coatings [107-111];
- the elaborated effective bioadhesive polymer films containing aprotinin for therapy of postoperational oncological patients.

Great attention is given to development of medicaments, promoting a rapid healing of wounds, burns and radiation lesions, efficiently applicable in field conditions and in reconstructive traumatic and plastic surgeries.

The new strategy is under development for wound healing by use of growth factors, such as protease, thrombin and peptides, the agonists of thrombin receptor out of the proteinase–activated receptor family (PAR) [112,113]. The methods have been elaborated to produce the preparations of PAR-agonistic peptides encapsulated in polymer compositions formed upon thermal precipitation of polyvinylcaprolactam hydrogel and in microcapsules of poly(d,l) lactide-co-glycolide [114,115]. The application of hydrogels with encapsulated peptides accelerated the wound healing in animals, which was due to intensified migration and proliferation of cells and due to neovascularization in the granulation tissue.

To-date, the medicinals in the form of dressings and tegumental materials, based on proteolytic complex of proteins immobilized on dialdehyde cellulose, are being produced from the wastes of crab products industry. The above means are effective for therapy of suppurative and burn wounds, for healing of postoperational cicatrices and bedsores. They are produced in industrial scale in the pilot plant at the Institute of Textile Fabrics [116-118]. The work has been started on creation of a new wound-healing means based on chitosan and proteolytic complex [119].

Researchers of the Kosygin Moscow State Textile University have been conducting the works on creation of new polymer materials, drug carriers. They offered the method for modification of chitosan films by a surfactant fostering the formation, on the film, of the layer acting as semi-permeable membrane to decelerate the curative agent wash-out from the organism [120,121]. Upon swelling, the film, as a whole, can increase its volume by 2 000–4 000%. By its capacity to absorb and retain moisture, the elaborated film is superior to all known dressings. It is especially effective for therapy of wounds difficult to heal in oncological patients.

Of great practical interest are the investigations on bacteriolytic microbial enzymes in view of possibility of their application as antimicrobial medicaments. The cultural fluid of *Lysobacter* bacteria was used to obtain the preparation "Lysoamidase" with a complex bacteriolytic activity [122]. The preparation contains the high-molecular weight acidic polysaccharide and about 20 proteins with various substrate specificities. The wide antimicrobial spectrum of the preparation is provided by a combined work of a few constituent bacteriolytic enzymes, including proteases. At present, studies are conducted to create the preparations specific for single species of bacteria and spores [123,124]. The scheme has been designed for purification and production, from "Lysoamidase", of four bacteriolytic enzymes with various substrate specificities to *S. aureus* cells. "Lysoamidase" and its constituent bacteriolytic enzymes can disrupt the vegetal cells of *B. cereus* and the spores of *B. subtilis*.

REFERENCES

[1] A.V Gusakov,. A.G. Berlin, N.N Popova, O.N Okunev, O.A.Sinitsyna, A.P. Sinitsyn: *Appl. Biochem. Biotechnol.,* 88, 119-126, (2000).

[2] N.V. Tsurikova, L. I. Nefedova, E.V. Kostileva et.al.: *Prikladnaya Biokhimiya i Microbiologiya* 38 (5), 502-508 (2002) (in Russian).

[3] A.P. Sinitsyn, A.V. Gusakov, O.A. Sinitsyna: Emerging Technologies & Trends In Garment Wet Processing. In *Proceedings of AATCC Symp., New Orleans, LA, USA, May 13-14, 1999, Emerging Technologies & Trends In Garment Wet Processing, AATCC Symp.*, New Orleans, LA, USA, May 13-14, 1999. 12-17 pp.

[4] V.A Baraznenok, E.G. Becker, N.V Ankudimova, O.N. Okunev: *Enzyme Microb. Technol.,* 25, 651-659 (1999).

[5] A.V. Gusakov, A.P. Sinitsyn, A.G. Berlin, N.N. Popova et al.: *Appl. Biochem. Biotechnol.*, 75, 279-293 (1998).

[6] Gusakov, A. Sinitsyn, S. Grishutin, D. Tikhomirov et al.: *Textile Chemist and Colorist & American Dyestuff Reporter,* 32(5), 42-47 (2000).

[7] O.F. Kastelyanos, O.V. Ermolova, A.P. Sinitsyn, N.N. Popova et al.: (1995) *Biochemistry* (Moscow), 60(6), 693-707 (1995) (Translated from *Biokhimiya*, 60(6), 925-943 (1995)).

[8] B. Gut'erres, A.P. Sinitsyn, O.F. Kastelyanos, A.G. Berlin et al.: *Prikladnaya Biokhimiya i Microbiologiya*, 34(6), 622-627 (1998) (in Russian).

[9] I.V.Solovyeva, O.N.Okunev, E.G.Krykova, G.A.Kochkina: *System. Appl. Microbiol.*, 22, 546-550 (1999).

[10] M.V.Semenova, S.G. Grishutin, A.V. Gusakov et al.: *Biokhimiya*, 68(5), 686-697 (2003) (in Russian).

[11] O.A. Sinitsyna, F.E. Buhtoyarov, A.V.Guasakov et al.: *Biokhimiya*, 68(11), 1494-1505 (2003) (in Russian).

[12] V.V.Lapin, N.A. Rodionova, N.A. Zagustina et al.: *Prikladnaya Biokhimiya i Microbiologiya* 38 (4), 452-454 (2002) (in Russian).

[13] N.A. Rodionova, N.V. Dubovaya, E.V. Eneiskaya, L.I. Martionivich, I.M. Gracheva, A.M. Bezborodov: *Prikladnaya Biokhimiya i Microbiologiya*, 36(5), 535-540 (2000) (in Russian).

[14] N.A. Rodionova, N.V. Dubovaya, N.I. Odintseva et al.: *Prikladnaya Biokhimiya i Microbiologiya* 38 (5), 490-494 (2002) (in Russian).

[15] S.V. Shleev, I. Gvon Khan, I.G. Gazaryan, O.V. Morozova, A.I. Yaropolov: *Applied Biochem. Biotech.*, 111(3), 167-183 (2003).

[16] S.V. Shleev, I. Gvon Khan, O.V. Morozova et al.: *Prikladnaya Biokhimiya i Microbiologiya,* 40(2), 165-172 (2004) (in Russian).

[17] S.V. Shleev, I.G. Gazaryan, E.S. Gorshina et al.: *Vestnik Moskovskogo Universita, Ser. 2, Khimiya*, 44(1), 35-39 (2003) (in Russian).

[18] V.I.Tishkov, A.G. Galkin, V.V. Fedorchuk et al.: *Biotechnology & Bioengineering*, 64(2), 187-193 (1999).

[19] U. Schwarz-Linek, A. Krodel, F.-A. Ludwig, A. Schulze, S. Rissom, U.Kragl, V.I. Tishkov & M. Vogel: *Synthesis*, 33(6), 947-951 (2001).

[20] A.M. Rojkova, A.G. Galkin, L.B. Kulakova, A.E. Serov, P.A. Savitsky, V.V. Fedorchuk & V.I. Tishkov: *FEBS Lett.*, 445(1), 183-188 (1999).

[21] K. Seelbach, B. Riebel, W.Hummel, M.R. Kula, V.I. Tishkov, A.M. Egorov, C. Wandrey & U. Kragl: *Tetrahedron Lett.*, 37(9), 1377-1380 (1996).

[22] V.I. Tishkov: *Bulletin of Moscow University, Ser. 2 Chemistry*, 43(6), 380-387 (2002).

[23] M.I.Youshko, L.M. van Langen, E. de Vroom, H.M. Moody, F. van Rantwijk, R.A. Sheldon, V.K. Švedas: *J. Molecular Catalysis B: Enzymatic*, 10, 509-515 (2000).

[24] M.I.Youshko, L.M. van Langen, E. de Vroom, F. van Rantwijk, R.A. Sheldon, V.K. Švedas: *Biotechnology & Bioengineering*, 73 (5), 426-430 (2001).

[25] M.I. Youshko, H.M. Moody, A.L. Bukhanov, W.H.J. Boosten & V.K. Švedas: *Biotechnol. Bioeng.*, 85(3), 323-329 (2004).

[26] M.I. Youshko & V.K. Švedas: *Adv. Synth. Cat.* 344 (8), 894-898 (2002).

[27] M.I. Youshko, G.G. Chilov, T.A. Shcherbakova, V.K. Švedas: *Biochim. Biophys. Acta. Proteins & Proteomics,* 1599 (1-2), 134-140 (2002).

[28] M.I. Youshko, A.L. Bukhanov, V.K. Švedas: *Biokhimiya,* 68(3), 334-338 (2003) (in Russian).

[29] V.G. Vinter, S.G. Fatkhov, R.Yu. Kozlova, V.S.Reznik, A.I. Konovalov: *RF Patent No 2174555* (2001).

[30] N.N. Kuznetsova, E.V. Nikolaeva, V.G. Vinter: Screening of microorganisms producing cyclodextrine glucotransferases. In *Proceedings of Int. Conference «New Geometry of Nature»*, Kazan, Russia, Aug. 25 – Sept. 5, 2003, Part 2, 190-193 pp.

[31] A.A. Mats, V.P. Murygina, R.S. Ivashko: *RF Patent No.2069492* (1996).

[32] A.A. Mats, V.P. Murygina, R.S. Ivashko: *RF Pat. No.2069493* (1996).

[33] V.P. Murygina, E.V. Korotaeva, A.V. Stolyarova, L.R. Peterson: *RF No.2090697* (1997).

[34] S. V. Kalyuzhnyi, M. A. Gladchenko, V. I. Sklyar, O. V. Kurakova, S. S. Shcherbakov: *Environ. Technol.,* 22, 919 (2000).

[35] S. V. Kalyuzhnyi, M. A. Gladchenko, V. I. Sklyar, Ye. S. Kizimenko, S. S. Shcherbakov: *Appl. Biochem. Biotechnol.*, 90, 107 (2001).

[36] S. Kalyuzhnyi, V. Sklyar, T. Mosolova et al.: *Wat. Sci. Technol.,* 42, 363 (2000).

[37] S. Kalyuzhnyi, V. Sklyar: *Wat. Sci Technol.,* 41(12), 23(2000).

[38] N.A Yemashova, A.F.Telegina, I.B. Kotova, S.V. Kalyuzhnyi: Degradation of azo dyes by methanogenic sludge. In *Proceedings of the 2nd Moscow Int. Congress "Biotechnology: State of the Art and Prospects of Development*", Moscow, Russia, Nov. 10-14, 2003, Part 2, 217 p.

[39] S.V. Popova, A.N. Epov, V.I. Sklyar, S.V. Kalyuzhnyi: Investigation of biological sulphide oxidation into elementary sulphur. In *Proceedings of the Intern. Conf. "Biocatalysis-2002: Fundamentals and Applications",* Moscow, Russia, June 22-27, 2002, 126 p.

[40] Kalyuzhnyi S.V. Biocatalysis for environmental protection. In *Proceedings of the 1st Moscow Int. Congress. "Biotechnology: State of the Art and Prospects of Development"*, Moscow, Russia, Oct. 14-18, 2002, 414 p.

[41] S.V. Popova, A.N. Epov, Sklyar, S.V. Kalyuzhnyi: *Kataliz v promyshlennosti*, 1 (2004) (in press) (in Russian).

[42] E. N. Efremenko, V. S. Sergeeva: *Izv. Akad. Nauk, Ser. Khim.,* 1743-1749 (2001).

[43] S.D. Varfolomeyev, E.N. Efremenko, T.K. Aliev, Yu.A.Votchitseva: *RF Paten Application No 2002131715*, Nov. 26, 2002.

[44] E.N. Efremenko, T.K. Aliev, Yu.A.Votchitseva, S.D. Varfolomeyev: *RF Paten Application No 2003136646,* Dec. 19, 2003.

[45] L.V. Lukachova, E.A. Kotel'nikova, D.D' Ottavi, E.E. Karyakina et al.: *IEEE Sensor J.,* 3(3), 326-333 (2003).

[46] E.A. Ulasova, D. Moscone, L. Micheli, L. Vāsii, G.G. Palleschi., S.V. Vdovichev, A. Zorin, S.A. Krutovertsev, E.E. Karyakina, A.A. Karyakin: *Electroanalysis*, 15(5), 1-5 (2003).

[47] F. Ricci, G. Palleschi, Y. Yigzaw, L. Gorton, T. Ruzgas, A. Karyakin: *Electroanalysis,* 15(3), 175-182 (2003).

[48] A.L.Gindilis, I.N. Kurochkin: *Prikladnaya Biokhimiya i Microbiologiya*, 34(3), 326 (1998) (in Russian).

[49] G.F. Makhaeva, L.V. Sigolaeva, L.V. Zhuravleva, A.V. Eremenko, I.N. Kurochkin, V.V. Malygin, and R.J. Richardson: *Journal of Toxicology and Environmental Health*, 66, *Part A*, 599-610 (2003).

[50] G.F. Makhaeva, L.V. Sigolaeva, L.V. Zhuravleva, A.V. Eremenko, I.N. Kurochkin, R.J. Richardson, V.V. Malygin: *ASA News Letters,* 05-2,16-21 (2002).

[51] G.F. Makhaeva, L.V. Sigolaeva, L.V. Zhuravleva, A.V. Eremenko, I.N. Kurochkin, R.J. Richardson and V.V. Malygin: Neuropathy target esterase in whole blood: biomarker for exposure to neuropathic organophosphorus compounds. In *Proceedings of CBMTS-Industry II: The World Congress on Chemical and Biological Terrorism*, 327-336 (2002).

[52] L.V. Sigolaeva, A. Makower, A.V. Eremenko, G.F. Makhaeva, V.V. Malygin, I.N. Kurochkin, F. Scheller: *Analytical Biochemistry*, 290(1), 1-9 (2001).

[53] L.V. Sigolaeva, A. Makower, A.V. Eremenko, G.F. Makhaeva, V.V. Malygin, I.N. Kurochkin, F. Scheller: *NeuroToxicology,* 21(4), 637-638 (2000).

[54] A.V. Eremenko, N. Kurochkin, L.V. Sigolaeva et al.: *Russian Chemical Journal of D.I. Mendeleyev Society* (2004) (in press) (in Russian).

[55] I.A. Budashov, I.N Kurochkin, V.V.Tsibezov, S.L. Kalnov, A.K. Denisov, O.I. Kiselyova, I.V. Yaminsky: *Membr. Cell Biol.,* 13(3), 397-409 (2000).

[56] I.N. Kurochkin: *Adv. in Biosensors*, 3, 77-109 (1995).

[57] I.N. Kurochkin, I.A. Budashov, A.B. Paval'ev, V.V. Skripnyuk, G.A. Shabanov: *Sensornye Sistemy*, 12(1), 122-134 (1998) (in Russian).

[58] A.B. Paval'ev, I.N. Kurochkin, S.F. Chernov: *Biolog. Membrany*, 15(3), 342-348 (1998) (in Russian).

[59] I.A. Budashov, I.N. Kurochkin, A.K. DENISOV, V.V. Skripnyuk, G.A. Shabanov: *J. Microbiol.*, 6, 11-15 (1997) (in Russian).

[60] I.A. Budashov, I.N. Kurochkin, V.V. Tsibezov et al.: *Biolog. Membrany*, 16(3), 325-336 (1999) (in Russian).

[61] I.N. Kurochkin: Nano reading Biosensor. In *Proceedings of the 2nd Moscow Int. Congress "Biotechnology: State of the Art and Prospects of Development*", Moscow, Russia, Nov. 10-14, 2003, Part 2, 180 p.

[62] B.B. Dzantiev, A.V. Zherdev, M.F. Yulaev, R.A. Sitdikov, N.M. Dmitrieva, I.Yu. Moreva: *Biosensors & Bioelectronics*, 11(1/2), 179-185 (1996).

[63] A.V. Zherdev, N.A. Bizova, A.I. Yaropolov, N.V. Lubimova, O.V.Morozova, B.B. Dzantiev: *Appl. Biochem. and Biotechnol.*, 76(3), 203-215 (1999).

[64] F. Garcia Sanchez, A. Navas Diaz, A.F. Gonzalez Diaz, M.C.Torijas, D.Alcantara, S.A. Eremin: *Anal.Chim.Acta*, V. 395, N 1, 133-142 (1999).

[65] F. Garcia Sanchez, A. Navas Diaz, A.F. Gonzalez Diaz, S.A. Eremin: *Anal.Chim.Acta,* V. 378, 219-234 (1999).

[66] E.V.Yazynina, A.V. Zherdev, B.B. Dzantiev, V.A. Izumrudov, S.J. Gee B.D. Hammock: *Anal. Chim. Acta.,* 399(1-2), 151-160 (1999).

[67] B.B. Dzantiev, A.V. Zherdev, O.G. Romanenko, L.A. Sapegova*: Int. J. of Environ. Anal. Chem.*, 65(1-4), 95-111 (1996).

[68] M.F. Yulaev, R.A Sitdikov, N.M.Dmitrieva, E.V.Yazynina, A.V. Zherdev, B.B. Dzantiev: *Sensors & Actuators B.*, 75(1-2), 129-135 (2001).

[69] E.V.Yazynina, A.V. Zherdev, B.B. Dzantiev, V.A. Izumrudov et al.: *Analytical Chemistry*, 71(16), 3538-3543 (1999).

[70] N.F. Starodub, B.B. Dzantiev, V.M. Starodub, A.V. Zherdev: *Anal. Chim. Acta,* 424(1), 37-43 (2000).

[71] S.A. Eremin, I.A. Ryabova, J.N.Yakovleva, E.V. Yazynina, A.V. Zherdev, B.B. Dzantiev: *Anal. Chim. Acta,* 468(2), 231-238 (2002).

[72] E.V.Yazynina, A.V. Zherdev, S.A. Eremin, V.A. Popova, B.B. Dzantiev: *Prikladnaya Biokhimiya i Microbiologiya,* 38 (1), 9-14 (2002) (in Russian).

[73] J.V. Samsonova, M.Yu. Rubtsova, L.A.Chikisheva, A.M. Egorov: *Vest. Mosk. Universit., Ser.2, Khimiya*, 43(6), 396-398 (2002) (in Russian).

[74] M.Yu. Rubtsova, Z.V. Samsonova, M.L. Bashkurov, L.V. Chikisheva, A.M. Egorov: Detection of antibiotics in milk by immunochemical methods. *Abstracts of VIIth International Conference on Agri-Food Antibodies*, Sept. 10-13, 2003, Uppsala, Sweden, P-06.

[75] M.Yu. Rubtsova, J.V. Samsonova, L.A.Chikisheva, A.A. Ezhov, A.M. Egorov: Dipstick tests for environmental monitoring and food quality control. *Abstracts of VIth International Conference on Agri-Food Antibodies*, October 3-5, 2001, Prague, Czech Republic, 53 p.

[76] A.A. Mart'ianov, A.V. Zherdev, S.A. Eremin, B.B. Dzantiev: *Analytical Chemistry,* (2004) (in press).

[77] A.A. Mart'ianov, B.B. Dzantiev, A.V. Zherdev, R. Cespedes, M. Petrovic, D. Barcelo: *Talanta*, (2004) (in press).

[78] J.V. Samsonova, C.T. Elliott, M. Franek: BIACORE biosensor immunoassay for 4-nonylphenols. *Abstracts of VIIth International Conference on Agri-Food Antibodies*, Sept.10-13, 2003, Uppsala, Sweden, P-05.

[79] E.I. Dement'eva, G.D. Kutuzova, I.A. Lundovskih, N.N.Ugarova: *RF Patent No 2164241* (1999).

[80] N.N. Ugarova, L.Yu. Brovko, E.I. Belyaeva, I.V. Berezin: *RF Patent No 1041568* (1993).

[81] L.Yu. Brovko, V.G. Froundjian, N.A. Romanova, N.N. Ugarova: *RF Patent No 2061045* (1996).

[82] L.Yu. Brovko, V.G. Froundjian, V.S. Babunova, N.N. Ugarova: *J. Dairy Research*, 66, 627-631 (1999).

[83] V.G. Froundjian, V.S. Babunova, N.N. Ugarova: *Vest. Mosk. Universit., Ser.2, Khimiya,* 43(6), 389-392 (2002) (in Russian).

[84] V.G. Froundjian, N.N. Ugarova, D.P. Trudil: In: *Bioluminescence & Chemiluminescence. Progress and Current Applications,* Eds.: Ph.E.Stanley and L.J. Kricka, World Scientific Publ. Co., 2002., 475- 478 pp.

[85] A.A. Karyakin, S.V. Morozov, E.E. Karyakina, S.D. Varfolomeyev, N.A. Zorin, S. Cosnier: *Electrochemistry Communications*, 4, 417–420 (2002).

[86] S.V. Morozov, P.M. Vignais, L. Cournac, N.A. Zorin, E.E. Karyakina, A.A. Karyakin, S. Cosnier: *International Journal of Hydrogen Energy*, 27, 1501–1505 (2002).

[87] A.A. Karyakin, S.V. Morozov, E.E. Karyakina, M. Yu. Vagin, S.D. Varfolomeyev: RF *Patent Application No 2003112989/13(014144),* 06.05.2003.

[88] A.V.Maksimenko, V.L.Golubykh, E.G.Tischenko: *Metab. Eng*., 5(3), 177 – 182 (2003).

[89] R.B. Aisina, L.I. Moukhametova, E.V. Firsova, S.D. Varfolomeyev: *Appl. Biochem. Biotechnol.*, 84, 1-4 (2000).

[90] R.B., Aisina, L.I. Moukhametova, S.D. Varfolomeyev: *Fibrinolysis and Proteolysis*, 14, Suppl.1, 42 (2000)

[91] L.I. Moukhametova, R.B. Aisina, S.D. Varfolomeyev: 14, Suppl. 1, 41 (2000).

[92] V.V. Vorontsov, K.B. Gershkovich, T.S. Sharkova, T.N. Serebryakova, R.B. Aisina: *Thrombosis, Hemostasis and Rheology,* 1, 83 (2001) (in Russian).

[93] K.B. Gershkovich, V.V. Vorontsov, R.B. Aisina, T.S. Sharkova, T.N. Serebryakova: *Thromb., Krovotoch. i Bolezni Sosudov, Moscow, Suppl.* 1, 53 (2002) (in Russian).

[94] K.B. Gershkovich, L.I. Moukhametova, V.V. Vorontsov, R.B. Aisina, T.N. Serebryakova, T.S. Sharkova: *Thromb., Krovotoch. i Bolezni Sosudov, Moscow, Suppl.* 2, 33-34 (2003) (in Russian).

[95] R.B. Aisina, L.I. Moukhametova, K.B Gershkovich, S.D. Varfolomeyev: *Thromb. Haemost., Suppl.* 1, 428 (2001).

[96] R. B. Aisina, L. I. Moukhametova, S.D. Varfolomeyev: *J. Thrombos. Haemost., Suppl.*, 1847 (2003).

[97] R.B. Aisina, O.Yu. Bulygin, L.I. Moukhametova, S.D. Varfolomeyev, A.N Mamaev, A.P. Momot: *RF Patent Application No 2003131105/15* (033476) 23.10.2003.

[98] S. Voronov, N. Zueva, V. Orlov, A. Arutyunyan, O. Kost: *FEBS Letters*, 522, 77-82 (2002).

[99] P.V. Binevski, E.A. Sizova, V.F. Pozdnev, O.A. Kost: *FEBS Lett.*, 550, 84-88 (2003).

[100] N.B. Chesnokova, A.B. Grigor'ev, T.A. Pavlenko, I.I. Nikol'skaya, O.A. Kost, N.F. Kazanskaya: *Vestnik RAMN*, 9, 29-32 (2003) (in Russian).

[101] I.P. Gladysheva, N.A. Moroz, T.A. Karmakova, E.R. Nemtsova et al.: *Journal of Drug Targeting*, 9, 303-316 (2001).

[102] I.P. Gladysheva, O.V. Polekhina, T.A. Karmakova, E.R. Nemtsova et al.: 74, 303-308 (2001).

[103] I.V. Berezin, V.V.Men'shikov, N.F. Kazanskaya, P.I. Tolstikh, N.I. Larionova et al.: *RF Patent No 960190* (1982).

[104] E.V. Malykh, O.P. Tiourina, Balabushevitch N.G., N.I. Larinova: *Biokhimiya*, 63(10), 1317-1319 (1998) (in Russian).

[105] N.I. Larionova, E.V. Malykh, A.Ju. Krasota, D. Duchene et al.: *Sci. Pharm.*, v. 69(3), p. 302-303 (2001).

[106] N.V. Larionova, E.V. Malykh, A.L. Villemson, A.Ju. Krasota et al.: *Int. J. Pharm.*, 256(1-4), 191-198 (2002).

[107] N.G. Balabushevitch, G.B. Sukhorukov, N.A. Moroz, N.I. Larionova et al.: *Biotechnology and Bioengineering*, 76(3), 207-213 (2001).

[108] O.P. Tiourina, A.A. Antipov, G.B. Sukhorukov, N.I. Larionova, Yu. Lvov, H. Mohwald: *Macromolecular Bioscience*, 1, 209-214 (2001).

[109] N.I. Larionova, D.V. Volodkin, N.G. Balabushevitch, G.B.Sukhorukov, H. Mohwald: *Sci. Pharm.*, 69(3), 175-176 (2001).

[110] D.V. Volodkin, N.G. Balabushevitch, G.B. Sukhorukov, N.I. Larionova: *STP Pharm. Sci.*, 13(3), 163-170 (2003).

[111] N.G. Balabushevich, O.P. Tiourina, D.V. Volodkin, N.I. Larionova, G.B. Sukhorukov: *Biomacromol.*, 4, 1191-1197 (2003).

[112] S.M. Strukova, T.N. Dugina, I.V. Chistov et al.: *Bioorgan. Khimiya*, 24, 288-292 (1998) (in Russian).

[113] S.M. Strukova: *Biokhimiya* 66(1), 8-18 (2001) (in Russian).

[114] E.A. Markvicheva, S.V. Kuptsova, T.Yu. Mareeva, A.A. Vikhrov et al.: *Appl. Biochem. Biotechnol.*, 88(1-3), 145-157 (2000).

[115] S.M. Strukova, T.N. Dugina, I.V. Chistov et al: *Clin. Appl. Thromb. Hemostasis*, 7(4), 325-329 (2001).

[116] A.A. Belov, V.N. Filatov, G.N. Donskih et al.: *Vestnik Mosk.Universit., Ser. 2, Khimiya,* 44(1), 16-19 (2003) (in Russian).

[117] V.N. Filatov, V.V. Ryl'tsev, A.A. Belov: *Nauka i Promysh. Rossii*, 2(3), 40-48 (2003) (in Russian).

[118] A.A. Belov, V.N. Filatov, L.A. Belova: Immobilization and characterization of a proteolytic complex isolated from the crustacean hepatopancreas and immobilized on textile carriers. In *Proceedings of the 1st Moscow Int. Congress. "Biotechnology: State of the Art and Prospects of Development"*, Moscow, Russia, Oct. 14-18, 2002, 72 p.

[119] A.A. Belov, V.N. Filatov, G.N. Donskih et al.: A new class of multienzymic wound dressings based on chitosan and other biodegradable polymers In *Proceedings of the Int. Confernce. "Bioresources, Biotechnologies and Innovations of the South Russia"*, Pyatigorsk, Russia, Oct. 21-24, 2003, Part 1, 33-37 pp.

[120] N. Kildeeva, G. Vichoreva, I. Gorbacheva, S. Rogovina, T. Acopova: Cellulose-chitosan composition in liquid and solid state. In: *Chitosan in Pharmacy and Chemistry*, Ed. R.A.A.Muzzarelli, and C. Muzzarelli, Atec, Italy, 2002, 245-249 pp.

[121] V. Babak, N. Kildeeva, E. Merkovitch, M. Rinaudo: Formation of enzyme delivery systems from chitosan-surfactant physical gel complexes. In: *Chitin Enzymology*. Ed. R.A.A.Muzzarelli, Atec, Italy, 2001, 591-594 pp.

[122] I.S. Kulaev, O.A. Stepnaya, Tsfasman I.M., T.S. Cheremenskaya, V.K. Akimenko, L.A. Ledova, L.G. Zubritskaya: *RF Patent No 2193063* (2002).

[123] E.A. Begunova, O.A. Stepnaya, V.Ya. Lysanskaya, I.S. Kulaev: *Biokhimiya*, 58(7), 896-901 (2003) (in Russian).

[124] B.V. Sitkin, V.Ya. Lysanskaya, I.M. Tsfasman, O.A. Stepnaya, I.S. Kulaev: *Microbiologiya*, 72(1), 136-137 (2003) (in Russian).

INDEX

E

F

G

H

I

K

L

M

N